The
Serious Jazz
Practice Book

Melodic Materials for the Modern Jazz Soloist

By BARRY FINNERTY

Editor and Publisher - Chuck Sher
Cover Graphics - Attila Nagy
Cover Artwork by Peaches, www.peachesstudio.com

ISBN 1-883217-42-3

For Clarita and Ruth...
The two ladies I adore
most in the world...
and without whom
this book would
not have been
possible.

Love you, B.

Special Thanks

SPECIAL THANKS: Chuck and Attila at Sher Music for all their help; Randy Vincent, Chuck Gee and Ruth Finnerty for their eagle-eyed proof reading; the people at Sibelius for their great tech support; Dave Creamer, who started me on this intervallic path long ago; Randy Brecker, Dave Liebman, Hubert Laws, Miles Davis, John Coltrane, and all the musicians who have been an inspiration to me over the years.

About The Author

Barry Finnerty is a guitar legend, having played and recorded with many of the best musicians in jazz and fusion—including Airto & Flora Purim, Chico Hamilton, Hubert Laws, Joe Farrell, Ray Barretto, Blood Sweat & Tears, Taj Mahal, the Thad Jones/Mel Lewis band, and Billy Cobham.

Barry was the guitarist on several seminal recordings in the 1970s and 1980s, including Miles Davis' "The Man With The Horn", the Brecker Brothers' "Heavy Metal Bebop" and the Crusaders' "Street Life".

Born in the San Francisco Bay Area, Barry moved to New York in 1973, played with the above-mentioned artists and many more, toured with the Crusaders for four years, and then moved back to the Bay Area in 1998, where he currently plays, composes, teaches and records. His latest records are available at www.barryfinnerty.com. He can be reached at barry@barryfinnerty.com.

Table of Contents

Foreword

In order to become an accomplished modern jazz soloist, one will need talent, inspiration, and imagination. One will have to have a lot of love for and dedication to the art of improvisation, of spontaneous musical creation. And one will have to have the FEELING! There are a lot of musical emotions and grooves that meet and interact in the world of jazz, but to me, the most important one, the one that imbues and informs all the others, is the feeling of the blues. Not always the NOTES of the blues, because jazz is a far more melodically and harmonically diverse kind of music, but the FEELING. Never forget that.

But also do not forget that to be a good modern jazz soloist, two things are required: mastering one's instrument and mastering one's materials. And for the modern jazz soloist, the two go hand in hand. In order for improvisational imagination to take flight, one needs to be able to play anything one can hear...to have so many possible note combinations under one's fingers, and to KNOW WHAT THEY ARE, WHAT THEY SOUND LIKE, and HOW TO USE THEM, that it becomes automatic.

The technique becomes a servant of the musical idea. The intellect and the emotion work together at such a high level that they are indistinguishable from one another. Creativity and inspiration rule.

But this book is not about musical intangibles. This book was written to give jazz players a thorough MUSICAL VOCABULARY for melodic improvisation, together with a solid WORKING KNOWLEDGE of their materials.

Part of this WORKING KNOWLEDGE will come from the fact that the student will have to do a lot of the WORK! For example, all of the diatonic, pentatonic, and arpeggio studies will have to be transposed and practiced through the other 11 keys. It is ABSOLUTELY ESSENTIAL that this be done if proper mastery of this method is to be achieved. The diminished studies will be transposed and practiced in the other two diminished scales, and the whole tone studies in the one other whole tone scale.

In the case of diatonic, you can photocopy each page and just add a key signature if you like, but I think the modern jazz soloist will get more out of it if he simply plays the scale of the key he is going to practice the exercise in, then works on the patterns until they become comfortable under his fingers. That way they will be better memorized, and he will better understand what they ARE, than if they were merely read off the page. Do it with your mind, your hands, and your instrument...you'll be better off! You could do the same thing with the diminished and whole tone exercises, but if it feels like too much of a brain drain, I recommend copying them out by hand.

NOTE: To teachers working from this book, or students working alone, I suggest focusing on one or two exercises at a time. Each one should be practiced through every possible applicable scale before moving on to the next one. Practice them slowly and evenly at first, then build up speed until you feel you have achieved command.

You will notice, as you go through the book, that every exercise has a NAME. I think this will also be helpful in establishing a working knowledge of the musical vocabulary we are laying out. The modern jazz soloist needs to have a practical understanding of his melodic materials. Having a handle on them will make them easier to use!

You may also notice, as I mention several times in the book, that NOT all the possible combinations and permutations of the various note groups have been included. This is INTENTIONAL. While it is true that there is enough stuff contained herein to keep most people practicing away for years, it is also true that there is a LOT more stuff out there. And I want YOU to find it! This book is not an encyclopedia; it is a practice guide based on a logical method of organizing notes for improvising that, if followed correctly, will surely pay HUGE dividends in your musicianship, no matter what instrument you happen to play.

All the patterns and exercises in the book are written out in 8th notes, mostly either as triplets or groups of 4 (there are a few odd 5's and 6's mixed in). They should be practiced as written, because 8th notes are the easiest way to insure that the notes will be securely under your fingers. BUT it is VERY IMPORTANT to remember that once the modern jazz soloist has learned his melodic materials, it is his (or her) sole responsibility to use them in a creative way. And endless strings of 8th notes are not particularly creative, at least from a rhythmic point of view.

So once you have practiced a particular bit of melodic material and have it securely under your fingers, a little rhythmic variation can open up those dull straight 8th notes into a world of melodic creativity! For example, let us take one of our most basic bits, the diatonic 4ths:

CD TRACK 1

Diatonic 4ths

Add a little bit of rhythmic bounce, and that same pattern can become:

An 8th note pattern of 4th descending while alternating up and down…

…can become this fairly modern-sounding beboppy little riff:

Take 8th note triplets or groups of five and play them in fours. Take fours and play them in triplets (examples of this sort of thing will appear later in the book). Develop motifs (see Appendix for more on this subject). Experiment with phrasing, rhythms, dynamics, and space. And those same principles apply to all the patterns and exercises in this book. All the raw materials are here for the learning. Their applications and various uses are the creative domain of the modern jazz soloist. So enjoy your study of these materials, practice them, learn them, and CREATE with them!

"The thing that distinguishes artists is the choices that they make"…my father, a wonderful actor, once told me that. Everyone has the same canvas and paints, the same blank page, or in the case of musicians, the same 12 notes to work with. So take these notes and go make some GOOD CHOICES! Good luck!

Section 1 - Diatonic Exercises

THE DIATONIC SCALES

Scales are the basic source from which all melodic materials are derived. The aspiring modern jazz soloist should have the knowledge of the diatonic scale throughout the range of his instrument, in all keys, before commencing these exercises.

For the sake of simplicity, these examples will be written in the key of C. However, it is recommended that they be applied to all the keys, and modified to fit the range of your particular instrument.

One can also take an exercise like the above, and play it not as triplets but in groups of 4.

There are plenty of ways to utilize your basic diatonic scale materials to make great jazz solos. We are going to get into a LOT of them later in this book. But for now, try practicing your scales as if they WERE a solo! Weave your way up and down, using DYNAMICS, soft to loud, loud to soft, and try to create some kind of melodic flow, while using ONLY the single note intervals within the scale.

There is some additional discussion of scales on **CD TRACK #2**

It is also permissible to throw in an interval jump or two, while focusing primarily on your scale-based melodic lines.

Another thing you can use to spice up your scale-based improvising is a little trill-type ornament. For example, a rather dull line such as:

...can sound a lot more melodic and soulful with the addition of the trill ornamentation:

Here is an exercise using this ornament through the scale:

Notice the chromatic approach notes on the ascending part. The chromatic scale is actually of immense value to the jazz improvisor. It can be used to connect tones of the scale from either above or below. There is an old Charlie Parker lick that is a good example of this:

So, except for the two places in the major scale where there are half steps (E to F and B to C, in the key of C, for example), the chromatic scale will bridge the gaps between the scale tones. And in those places, you can always add a chromatic approach note from the other direction:

When you are doing an upward chromatic approach, you can use the same 2-note lead-up throughout:

2 up and one down, or 2 down and one up:

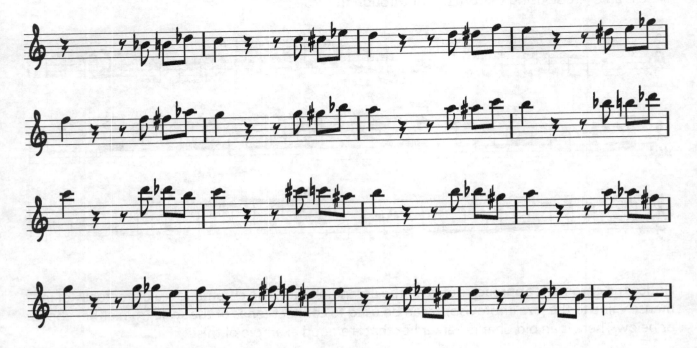

3 up and one down, or 3 down and one up:

We will deal with the melodic possibilities that spring from the chromatic scale a LOT more later in this book. But it is important to study and be always aware of this extremely useful aspect of it: Every scale tone can be connected to the next by one or two half steps. It's the shortest distance between two musical points.

Bebop Etude in C

Before we move on to the interval studies, which are the most basic, important and valuable raw melodic materials for the modern jazz soloist, here are a few more scale exercises that you might find useful:

Groups of 4 inside a 3rd

Groups of 5

Groups of 6

6

DIATONIC INTERVAL STUDIES

The goal of the modern jazz soloist should be to play his musical ideas as quickly and freely as his imagination can hear them. This requires him to have a huge number of note combinations under his fingers, ready to be played at a moment's notice. The following interval studies will be of considerable value in achieving that purpose.

4ths

4ths reversed

4ths alternating

4ths, 2 up one down

4ths w/chromatic approach

4ths w/dual chromatic approach

8

4ths w/chromatic connections

5ths

5th ersed

5ths alternating

5ths 2 up one down

5ths w/chromatic approach

5ths w/dual chromatic approach

(continued)

5ths w/chromatic connections

6ths

6ths reversed

6ths alternating

6ths, 2 up one down

10

It is important to remember that these interval studies are not just exercises to be played off the page; they are the raw materials to infuse your solos with true musicality! Play them through all the keys, and (string players) through all the positions. Practice them until they are comfortable under your fingers. Then, use them creatively! Here are some more:

6ths alternating up/down/up

6ths w/chromatic approach

6ths w/dual chromatic approach

6ths w/chromatic connections

Sevenths and octaves, in general, are not as handy for soloing as the smaller intervals, but they are still worth practicing...you never know when you might need them!

7ths

7ths reversed

7ths alternating

7ths w/chromatic approach

Octaves

Octaves reversed

Octaves alternating

Octaves w/chromatic approach

Octaves reversed w/ 2 note chromatic approach

Octaves w/chromatic slur on top

As I said in the foreword, it is up to the player to add variety and rhythmic creativity to transform these raw melodic materials from exercises into MUSIC. Here is an example using a few of the basic diatonic interval patterns we just learned to make a little solo on a blues in C. (Remember, the scales will change with the chords!) - **CD TRACK #3**

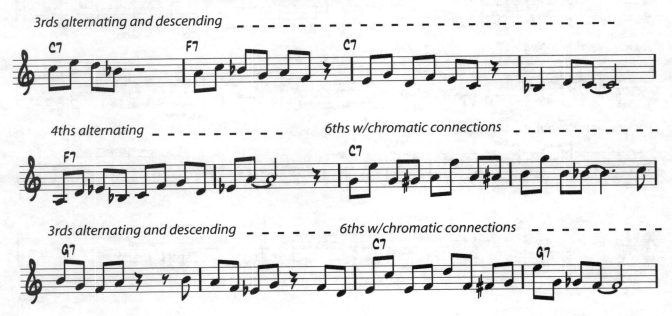

DIATONIC TRIAD STUDIES

Once we have thoroughly studied the 2-note intervals within the diatonic scale, it is time to move on to 3-note groups: triads. There is a wealth of melodic material to be found in the various combinations and permutations of these simple chords, as we shall see. Again, it is up to the individual musician to do his homework, and transpose each exercise into all the keys, and through the range of his instrument.

14

Triads in 4's

Triads w/chromatic approach

Triads reversed w/chromatic approach

Triads 1st inversion

Triads 1st inversion reversed

Triads 1st inversion broken

Triads 1st inversion in 4's

Triads 1st inversion w/chromatic approach

16

Triads 1st inversion reversed w/chromatic approach

Triads 2nd inversion

Triads 2nd inversion reversed

Triads 2nd inversion broken

Triads 2nd inversion in 4's

Triads 2nd inversion 4's off top note

Triads 2nd inversion 4's w/chromatic approaches

Triads 2nd inversion w/chromatic approach in middle

18

For a fast straight-ahead modal number like John Coltrane's "Impressions", some of the triads with chromatic approaches might be just what the doctor ordered! (We'll take this example from the second 8 bars so you can see the modulation.) - **CD TRACK #4**

Howard Roberts was really a great guitar player, and one of my earliest jazz influences. His first guitar clinic, 1969: I'm wearing the black and white striped shirt, standing to the left of Howard (he's the one with the shades). Lee Ritenour, who could already play and read his ass off at 17 (way better than me) is third from the left, standing up.

SPREAD TRIADS

Spreading out your triad voicings can also create some very pretty melodic effects:

Spread triads

Spread triads reversed

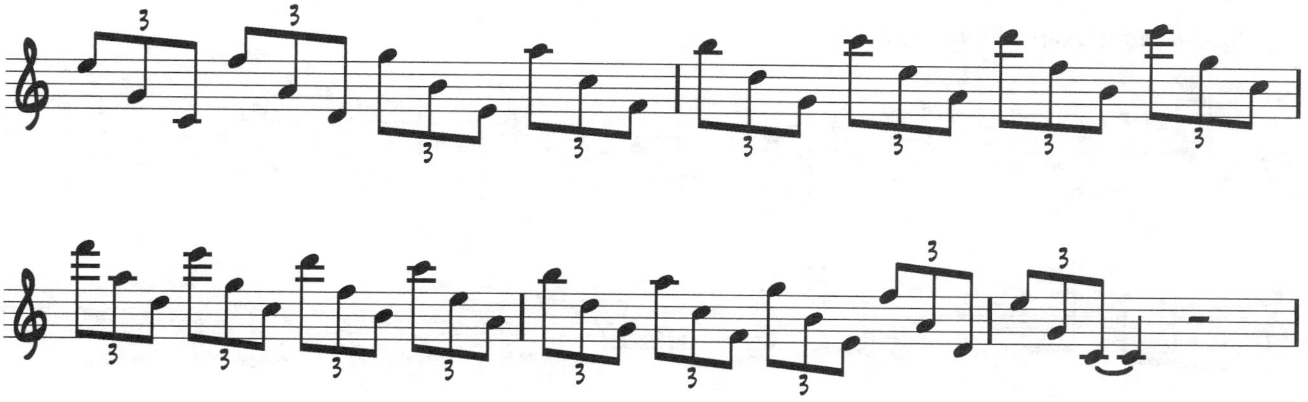

Spread triads alternating

Spread triads broken w/ chromatic approach on middle note

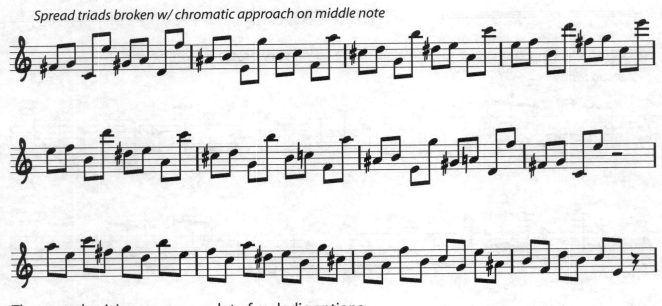

The spread voicings open up a lot of melodic options:

Spread triads alternating a 3rd apart (diatonically)

The inversions of the spread triad voicings are also nice:

Spread triads 1st inversion

Spread triads 1st inversion reversed

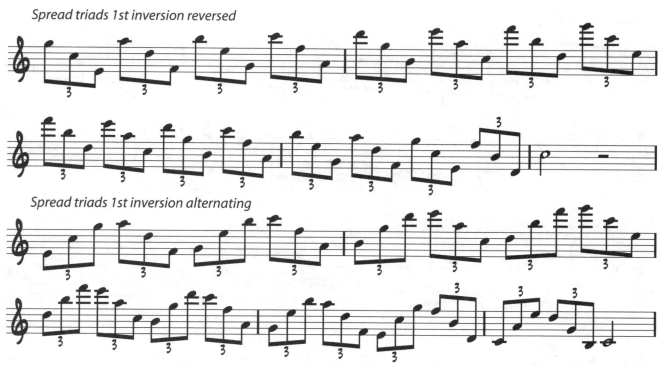

Spread triads 1st inversion alternating

There are plenty of possibilities for various chromatic approaches with the spread voicings.
I encourage you to find some of your own!

Spread triads 1st inversion w/ chromatic approach

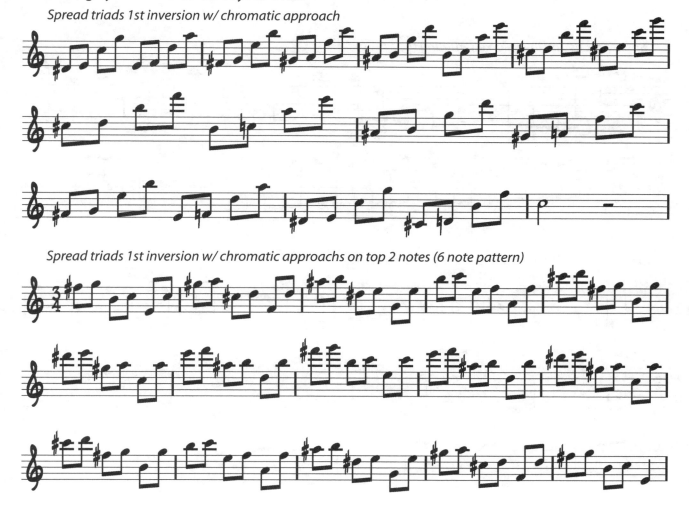

Spread triads 1st inversion w/ chromatic approachs on top 2 notes (6 note pattern)

22

Spread triads 2nd inversion

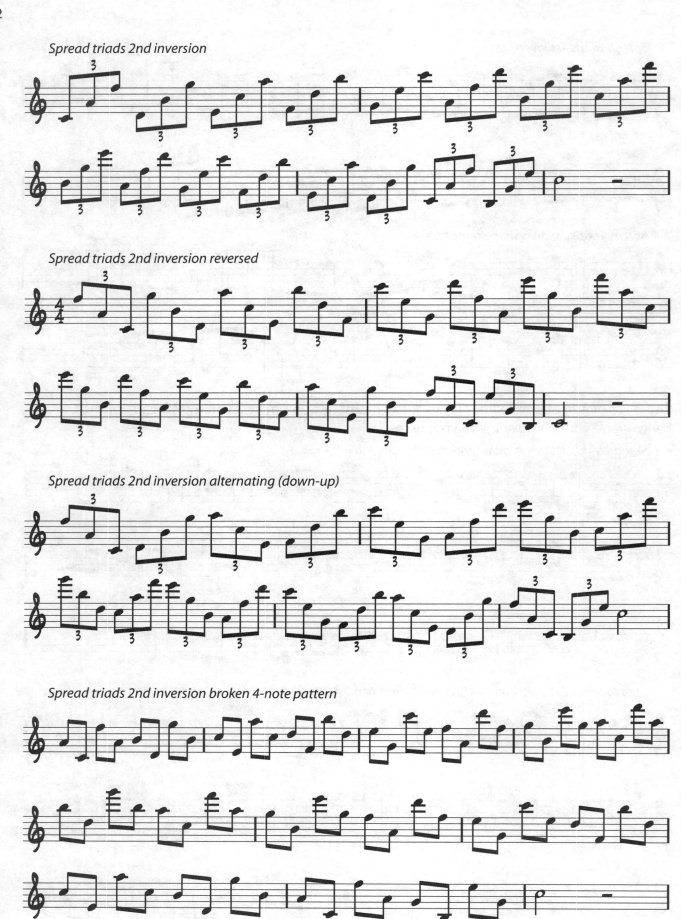

Spread triads 2nd inversion reversed

Spread triads 2nd inversion alternating (down-up)

Spread triads 2nd inversion broken 4-note pattern

Spread triads 2nd inversion w/chromatic approach (reversed descending)

This was from Feb. 28 and 29, 1984, at 55 Grand, New York. Jaco was starting his really crazy period, but was still functional. Mike Stern also played guitar on this gig, with Richie Morales on drums and Randy Brecker. I liked Jaco… our birthdays were 2 days apart…same year. (Photo by Jon Hammond).

24

QUARTAL TRIADS

Quartal triads (triads built in intervals of 4ths insteads of 3rds) are very important. The modern jazz soloist will find them indispensable to his melodic repertoire!

Quartal triads alternating ascending and descending in 3rds

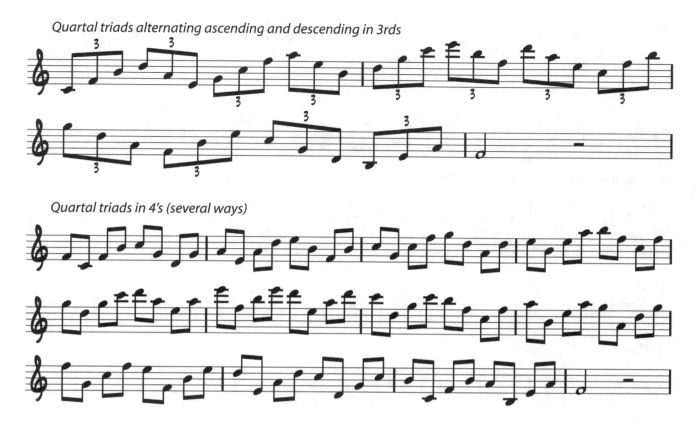

Quartal triads in 4's (several ways)

The inversions of the quartal triads are unique—a fourth followed by a second (1st inversion), or a second followed by a fourth (2nd inversion)—yet they can still yield a lot of good melodic material. (NOTE: Don't forget—all the patterns written in triplets can also be played as 8th notes in groups of 4!)

Quartal triads 1st inversion

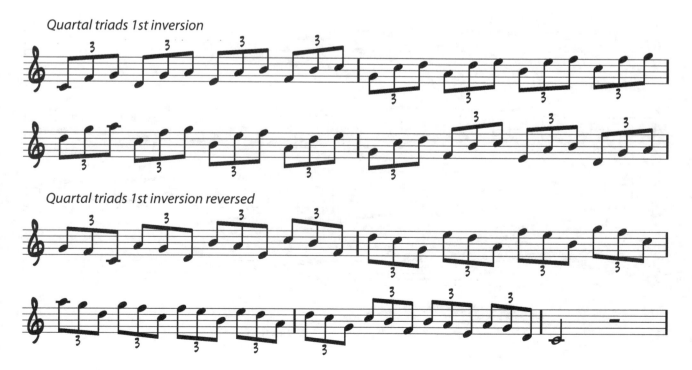

Quartal triads 1st inversion reversed

26

Quartal triads 1st inversion in 4's

Quartal triads 1st inversion ascending and descending in 3rds (in 8th notes)

Quartal triads 2nd inversion

Quartal triads 2nd inversion reversed

Quartal triads 2nd inversion ascending and descending in 3rds

The diatonic interval and triad patterns are essential tools to learn your instrument. But they will also work quite well "right out of the box" on tunes with open modal-type chord changes. You might want to try something with the quartal triads on a tune such as Herbie Hancock's "Maiden Voyage" - **CD TRACK #5**

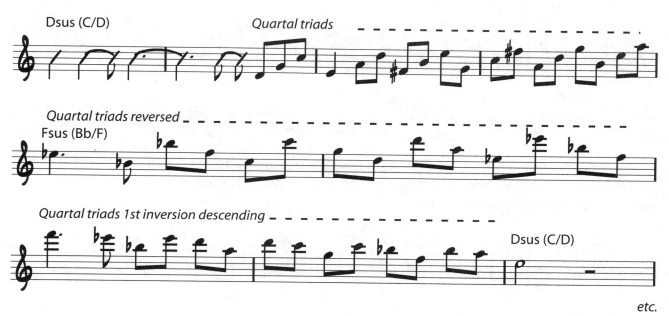

etc.

DIATONIC INTERVAL VARIATIONS

Not all of the possible combinations of interval and triad-based patterns are inherently suited for soloing; indeed, some feel very mechanical to play. But once the player has understood the CONCEPT of organizing groups of notes in this way, a whole world of melodic diversity is opened up for exploration! Here are a few more examples to whet your intervallic appetite:

4ths ascending and descending in 3rds

5ths w/dual chromatic approach in 3rds

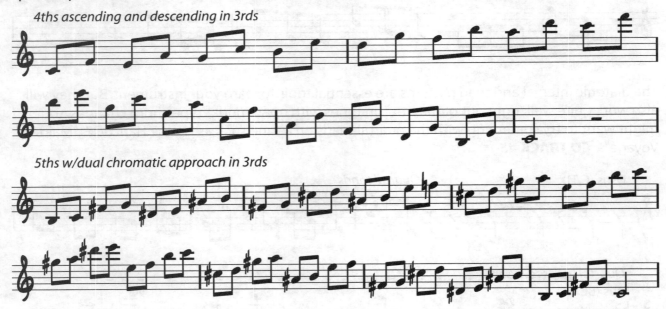

The larger intervals (5ths, 6ths, 7ths) seem to lend themselves more easily to larger melodic jumps. Even if, as now, we are restricting ourselves to the diatonic scale, we can find a lot of really interesting stuff to play! Such as:

6ths in 3rds

7ths in 3rds

A 7th and a 6th a 3rd apart, ascending and descending diatonically

Three 6ths a 5th apart ascending in 3rds, descending diatonically

A 7th and a 6th a 6th apart ascending in 3rds, descending diatonically

7ths a 5th apart

Double 5ths

Circle of 5ths and 4ths (up two 5ths, down two 4ths, down two 4ths, up one 5th descending)

Circle of 4ths and 5ths (down two 4ths, up two 5ths)

Circle of 4ths and 5ths (up 4, down 4, and vice versa)

Up four 5ths, down four 4ths (ascending diatonically)

Down five 4ths, up three 5ths (descending diatonically)

31

Circle of 4ths and 5ths (3 up, 2 down and vice versa)

Frank Gravis, Crazy Barry, and Graham Hawthorne. We rocked! Lazy Larry (featured on nothing!) didn't make the photo shoot. (Photo by Jon Hammond).

DIATONIC 7th CHORDS

Let us also take a look at the various melodic permutations of seventh chords when taken through the diatonic scale:

Diatonic 7th chords

Diatonic 7th chords reversed

Diatonic 7th chords broken

33

Diatonic 7th chords broken reversed

Diatonic 7th chords w/chromatic approach in 5's

We will explore the melodic possibilities that spring from individual arpeggios later in this book. But it is never a bad idea to run your diatonic 7th chord arpeggios through the full range of your instrument. And don't forget those 11 other keys!

Diatonic 7th chords in 2 octaves

34

Diatonic 7th chords spread out and broken (or: a 7th down and a 6th up, a 5th apart!)

I got my first electric guitar for my 14th birthday and my band in Hong Kong, The New Breed, opened the show for Herman's Hermits! Afterward I was mobbed by Chinese girls and signed a bunch of autographs. I was hooked on the music biz! I also got Herman's autograph and that of his lead guitarist, Derek Leckenby.

Section 2 - The Pentatonic Scale

Before we proceed to the arpeggios and the melodic materials of the whole tone, diminished, and chromatic scales, I thought it would be a good idea to take a look at probably the most useful of all melodic tools for the jazz soloist, the pentatonic scale. It is used not only in jazz, but in blues, rock, country and western, Chinese music...you name the style, the pentatonic scale will probably be the scale the soloist is using! Here are some of its permutations:

Pentatonic 4's

Pentatonic 4's reversed

Pentatonic 4's broken

36

Pentatonic 4's broken one note higher

Pentatonic 4's broken one note higher than that

Pentatonic scale in 5's

Pentatonic triplet lick

Pentatonic ascending one interval up

Pentatonic ascending two intervals up

Another handy pentatonic lick

38

Pentatonic groups of 6

The pentatonic exercises pretty much speak for themselves. They are the basic vocabulary of so many musical styles, and it is vital to have them down in all the keys. Then, I must emphasize again that it is your own creativity, phrasing, dynamics, and FEELING that will give life to these simple patterns. **CD TRACK #6**

8 bar pentatonic phrase

Remember that your C major (A minor) pentatonic can do double duty on F major7 (where it becomes 2-3-5-6-7) and Bb major7(b5) (where it becomes 2-3-b5-6-7).

4 bar pentatonic phrase (play Fma7 or Bbma7 (b5)

The modern jazz soloist also has the option of using one of the pentatonic patterns and switching between two different scales a half step apart (a minor 3rd or a tritone apart is good too). This can give a nifty "inside-outside" effect.

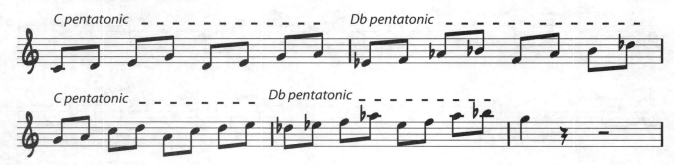

Section 3 - Arpeggio Studies
TRIADS

A command of arpeggios is also essential to the modern jazz soloist. Whatever key you are playing in, whatever chord you are improvising over, nothing will MELODICALLY define that HARMONIC TERRITORY like the correct arpeggio. Again, it is up to you to run these ideas through all the keys and the full range of your instrument.

Major triplets

Major 8th notes

Major w/chromatic approach

Major broken

40

Major broken w/dual chromatic approach

Major broken w/chromatic approach below and diatonic descending tone above

Minor triplets

Minor 8th notes

Minor w/chromatic approach

Minor broken

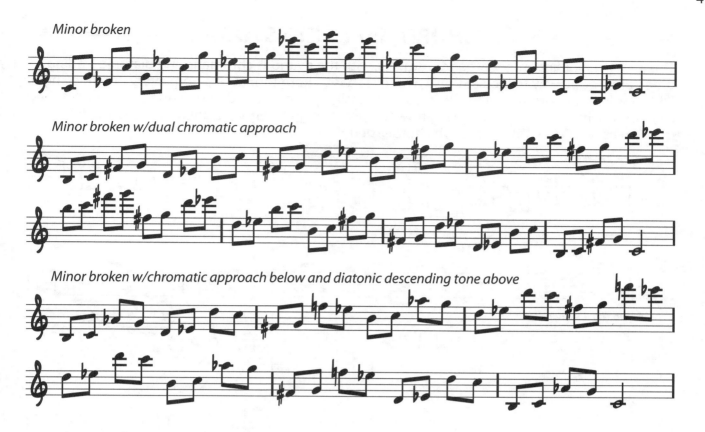

Minor broken w/dual chromatic approach

Minor broken w/chromatic approach below and diatonic descending tone above

This is me at 14, in Hong Kong, with the $40 St.George classical guitar my mother got me for my 13th birthday. She wanted me to be like Segovia. I wanted to be like the Beatles!

7th CHORD ARPEGGIO STUDIES

The above major and minor arpeggio studies, with their various chromatic and diatonic leading tones, are a good way to look at these two most basic chord formations from every possible angle. If you cycle them through all the keys, you can easily spend all day doing it! And at the end of the day, you will have a very good idea of how to make a melody with harmonic content. The following studies will deal with various 7th chord arpeggios:

Major 7th 4's

Major 7th 4's reversed

Major 7th 4's up and down

Oh, and it goes without saying...that's why I'm saying it now...that ALL your arpeggios should be run up and down the range of your instrument....preferably BEFORE you practice the broken up exercises on them. Look at the whole, then divide and conquer!

Major 7th arpeggio

Major 7th arpeggio reversed groups

Major 7th 6's

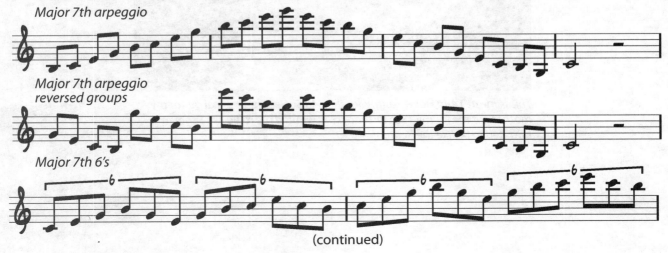

(continued)

43

Minor 7th arpeggio

Minor 7th 4's

Minor 7th 4's reversed

Minor 7th 4's up and down

Minor 7th 6's

Dominant 7th arpeggio

Dominant 7th 4's

Dominant 7th 4's reversed

Dominant 7th 4's up and down

Dominant 7th 6's

45

You can use your dominant 7th arpeggios (with an occasional chromatic approach) to create wonderful melodic solos on the blues. You can turn them around, make motifs out of them, mix their notes up any way you like. Just make sure you switch your arpeggios where the chords change: - **CD TRACK #7**

46

Minor 7th (b5) arpeggio (half-diminished)

Minor 7th (b5) 4's

Minor 7th (b5) 4's reversed

Minor 7th (b5) 4's up and down

Minor 7th (b5) 4's broken

Minor 7th (b5) 6's

You will notice that the arpeggio exercises (except the C and Cma7th) are not technically in the KEY of C. They are being written from the NOTE of C simply so they will occupy the same position on the staff. It is very important to look at your arpeggios from a variety of angles...that is, to analyze them from the point of view of different bass notes. Then they will take on a multitude of uses! For example, the C major triad will become Dsus4, Fma9, or Ami7 when used over those respective bass notes. Cm7(b5) will become Ebmi6 or Ab7(9). This kind of knowledge is essential to the intelligent use of arpeggios in improvisation by the modern jazz soloist! Here are some more good ones, each with just a couple of melodic examples. You can take them through the same variations as the previous arpeggios.

Cma7(b5)

Cma7(b5) example 1

Cma7(b5) example 2

Cma7(#5)

Cma7(#5) example 1

Cma7(#5) example 2

Cmi (ma7)

Cmi (ma7) example 1

Cmi (ma7) example 2

NOTE: I would have included the Cmi6 arpeggio here, but since it is identical to the Am7(b5), and you will have already practiced the previous exercises in all the keys (!), we will now proceed to the:

C7(b5)

C7(b5) example 1

C7(b5) example 2

Here's my psychedelic jazz/funk jam trio Deep Down & Out after a recent San Francisco performance of the interactive art/jazz event: Visible Sound! From the left: drummer Ronnie Smith, our special guest trombonist Conrad Herwig, me, bassist John Whitelaw, and the artist Tom Reyes.

50

QUARTAL ARPEGGIOS

The quartal arpeggios are also invaluable to the modern jazz soloist, especially the perfect 4th version, each of which fits into 5 keys! (For example, this one will work in the modes of F, Bb, Eb, Ab and Db!)

Quartal arpeggio

Quartal arpeggio in 3's

Quartal arpeggio in groups of 4

Quartal arpeggio (tritone-4th)

Quartal arpeggio (tritone-4th) triplets played in 4's

Quartal arpeggio (4th-tritone)

Quartal arpeggio (4th-tritone) in groups of 4

DIMINISHED AND AUGMENTED ARPEGGIOS

Much more will be explored regarding the analysis and various uses of these harmonic materials for creating melodies in the companion volume to this book, "Harmonic Possibilities of the Improvised Line". But while we are on the subject of arpeggios, let us not forget two of the most useful of all: the diminished and augmented chords. Since they spring from the symmetrical diminished and whole-tone scales, there are fewer of them to study: only 3 diminished and 4 augmented arpeggios. But since ANY of the notes can be the root, they are also supremely versatile!

C diminished 7th

C diminished 7th in 4's

C diminished 7th broken (tritones ascending in minor 3rds)

C diminished 7th broken reversed

52

C diminished 7th broken alternating

C diminished 7th (major 6ths ascending in minor thirds)

C diminished 7th (major 6ths alternating)

C diminished 7th spread voicing (major 6ths a tritone apart) in minor 3rds

Because the diminished and augmented arpeggios are SYMMETRICAL (made up of identical intervals) any part of the chord can be moved around in those interval steps...minor 3rds, tritones, and major 6ths in the case of diminished, and major 3rds and minor 6ths (augmented 5ths) in the case of augmented. This principle also applies to any parts of their corresponding scales, as we shall see in the following sections!

C diminished 7th spread voicing (tritones a major 6th apart) in minor 3rds

C diminished 7th spread voicing (major 6ths) in minor 3rds

C augmented

C augmented example 1

C augmented example 2

C augmented broken

C augmented broken (minor 6ths in major 3rds)

C augmented broken (minor 6ths in major 3rds alternating)

C augmented broken (2 minor 6ths in major 3rds)

The augmented chord also lends itself well to the chromatic approach:

C augmented triads w/lower chromatic approach

C augmented triads w/upper chromatic approach

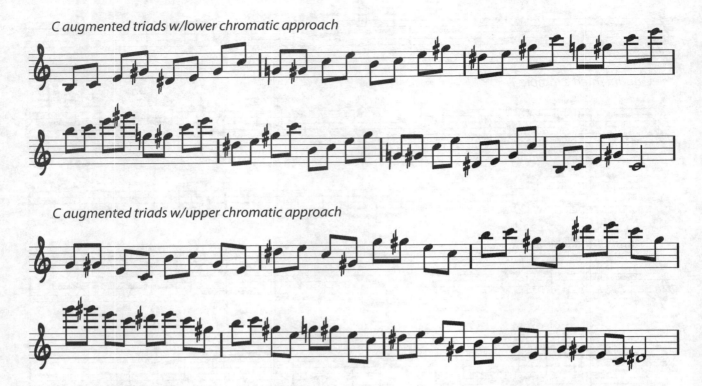

And here is a variation on the augmented arpeggio, with a chromatic approach before each note. It can be viewed as two augmented arpeggios a half step apart, but is more widely known as "the scale of half steps and minor thirds."

Scale of 1/2 steps and minor 3rds (C augmented w/chromatic approach on every note)

Scale of 1/2 steps and minor 3rds - example 1

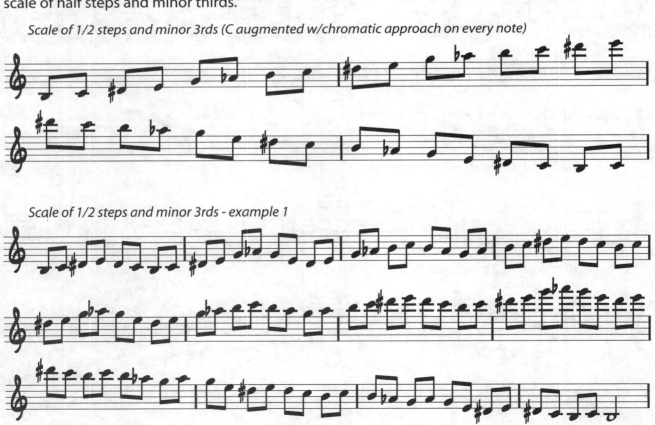

Scale of 1/2 steps and minor 3rds - example 2 (outlining the chord)

The use of arpeggios in improvisation is a very big subject and I plan to expound on it in much more detail in my next book. But for now, suffice it to say that if you have learned all your arpeggios in all the keys, you will have at your disposal at least 3 or 4 notes that will NEVER BE WRONG when you see a particular chord change. You can use the arpeggio notes to form the backbone of your solo, and your playing will be strong harmonically, even if the changes are quite advanced. Here is an example on Joe Henderson's "Inner Urge" using ALL arpeggio notes: - **CD TRACK #8**

Section 4 - The Whole Tone Scale

Now we will take a look at the melodic possibilities yielded by the whole tone scale. It is a symmetrical scale consisting of six notes in whole step intervals, any one of which can be regarded as the root. It is worth noting that there are only two possible whole tone scales in the 12-note chromatic scale. Melodic combinations of the two whole tone scales will be explored in the chromatic scale section of this book. But, to start, let us look at the basic whole tone scale from middle C:

C whole tone 4's alternating

C whole tone 3's alternating

C whole tone 6's descending

58

WHOLE TONE INTERVAL STUDIES

Now let us explore the interval combinations of the whole tone scale in the same way as we did with the diatonic scale earlier in the book.

Major 3rds in whole steps

Major 3rds in whole steps alternating

Tritones in whole steps

Tritones in whole steps alternating

Minor 6ths in whole steps

Minor 6ths in whole steps alternating

Minor 7ths in whole steps

Minor 7ths in whole steps alternating

The intervals of the whole tone scale can also sound very nice when chromatic connections and approaches are used.

Major 3rds in whole steps w/chromatic connection

60

Tritones in whole steps w/chromatic connection

Tritones in whole steps w/lower chromatic approach

Tritones in whole steps w/upper chromatic approach

Minor 6ths in whole steps w/chromatic connection

Minor 6ths in whole steps w/lower chromatic approach

WHOLE TONE TRIAD STUDIES

Building chords in 3rds from the whole tone scale produces a continuous pattern of augmented triads a whole step apart. These can make for some interesting melodic material:

Augmented triads in whole steps alternating

Augmented triads in 4's

Augmented triads in 4's broken

(continued)

4 note augmented chords alternating

Here's me with one of my biggest guitar heroes, the great George Benson!

WHOLE TONE VARIATIONS

You can do a lot of fun things with the whole tone scale. Since the dominant7(b5) arpeggio is one of its chord forms, you can move it around in whole steps:

Dominant 7(b5) chords in whole steps

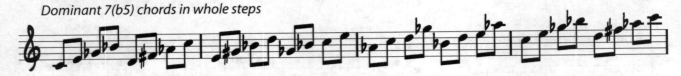

Or you can take the same arpeggio and break up the intervals, giving you, for example, two tri-tones, one down, one up, a major 3rd apart, in whole steps:

Dominant 7(b5) chords broken in whole steps

Here are a couple more whole tone exercises that you might find amusing:

You figure it out!

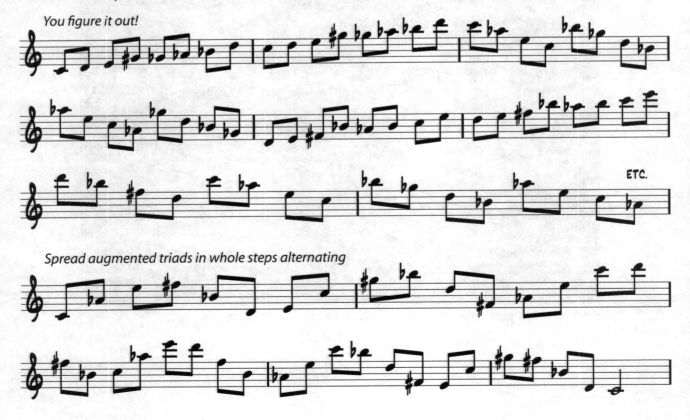

Spread augmented triads in whole steps alternating

Spread augmented triads a tritone apart, in major 3rds

And another variation on the dominant7(b5) arpeggio, this time breaking it into two minor 6ths, one down, one up, ascending and descending in major 3rds:

Minor 6ths a tritone apart, in major 3rds

The important thing to remember with the whole tone scale is that ANY note group that you make with the scale can then be moved around by ANY of the intervals within the scale! Let us take, for example the note group C-D-Bb-C:

In whole steps

In major thirds

In tritones

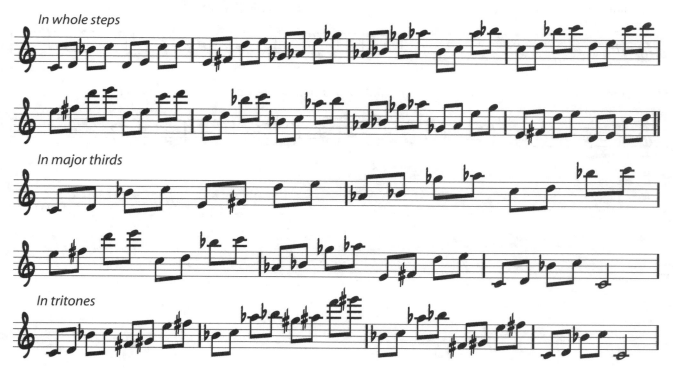

Besides its obvious use as the scale of the augmented chord, the whole tone scale can be used to extend the tonality of any dominant 7th chord. It has the 1, 2, 3, and b7, with the addition of the b5 and b6 which give it its unique color. Therefore, it works particularly well against any dominant 7(b5) or (#5) chord. Here is an example using the changes of the Jobim tune, "Desafinado".

CD TRACK #9

You can do the same sort of thing on Duke Ellington's "A Train". – **CD TRACK #10**

Section 5 - The Diminished Scale

The diminished scale is one of the most useful tools for the modern jazz soloist, because of its symmetry and its unmatched versatility. A diminished chord will resolve easily to almost any other chord, due to its 4 possible roots and the fact that it also can substitute for 4 possible dominant 7th chords, since every diminished 7th chord is a dominant7(b9) without the root. (Drop any of the tones in a diminished 7th chord one half step and you will get a dominant 7th in the key of the note you resolved to.) This makes the diminished scale both a great connector between chord changes in any key, and a good choice for soloing on all kinds of dominant 7th chords, including 7(b5), 7(b9), 7(#9), 13(b9) and 13(#9)... (the notable exception being the augmented 7th (7(#5)) chord...for that you must use the whole tone scale, or in the case of 7(#5b9) and 7(#5#9), the altered 7th scale).

Let's take a look at our basic raw material, the C (also Eb, Gb, and A) diminished scale:

Symmetrical construction...whole step, half step all the way...that is the essence of the diminished scale. This one is clearly the scale of choice to use on C, Eb, Gb, and A diminished 7th chords. Which, as we said, will resolve almost anywhere. But if we shift the orientation of the scale to start from the HALF STEP, it becomes easier to see the roots of the dominant 7th chords (in this case B7, D7, F7 and Ab7), each one followed by the b9, #9, major 3rd, b5, 5, 6 (or13), and b7, in their respective keys!

Of course, in the above example the 1's can also start on the F and the G# (Ab) and the relationships will stay the same. There is still another way to look at the diminished scale. It can be seen as the combination of the first four notes of two minor scales, a tritone apart:

DIMINISHED SCALE STUDIES

In any case, let us start with some scale exercises to gain fluidity within the diminished scale. And don't forget: there are two other diminished scales, in C# (also E, G, Bb) and in D (also F, Ab, B) that you will need to study with equal dedication if you want your mastery of this scale to be undiminished!

There are a lot more diminished scale exercises you can practice if you are so inclined...such as:

Or this one, with an ornament:

With the Crusaders. This was actually from Joe Sample's "Rainbow Seeker" session in 1977. I didn't join the band until 1979, when they did "Street Life". I think this pic appeared in Record World *magazine.*

DIMINISHED INTERVAL STUDIES

But now it is time to move on to our melodic meat and potatoes, so to speak, and explore the intervallic possibilities that spring from the diminished scale. We can do this in much the same way as we did with the diatonic and whole tone scales, but there are some interesting differences, as we shall see. We will start with the interval of the minor 3rd, the basic building block of the diminished chord:

Minor 3rds in diminished scale steps

Minor 3rds in diminished scale steps alternating

Now, we can see that the minor 3rd interval can be played melodically through all the steps of the scale. This will also be true of the other intervals contained in the basic diminished chord, that is, the tritone and the major 6th. This is due to the symmetrical nature of the scale. The notes of the C diminished chord - (C, Eb, F#, A) when combined with those of the D diminished chord - (D, F, Ab, B) form the C diminished scale. But (and this is a very big but!) there are many intervals produced by the diminished scale...major 3rd, 4th, perfect 5th, minor 6th, minor and major 7th...that will NOT go symmetrically up the scale. For example, if you try to make a pattern of major 3rds through the diminished scale, you get:

Major 3rds and 4ths in diminished scale steps

Which can produce some interesting results. Notice that you can also look at it as a 4-note pattern moving in minor 3rds:

Major 3rds and 4ths alternating

Major 3rds and 4ths alternating reversed

So if you want to take major 3rds or virtually any interval or combination of intervals from the diminished scale, and play with them, you can always do it in minor 3rds:

Major 3rds in minor thirds

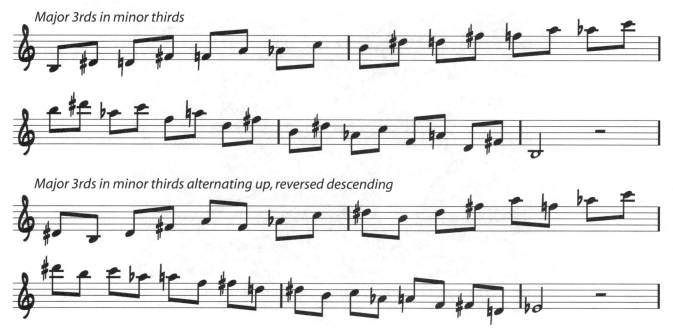

Major 3rds in minor thirds alternating up, reversed descending

The 4th is another interval that does not go up the diminished scale in a symmetrical way. But you could think of this pattern as a little 4-note blues lick, going b7-b3-3-1, starting on D7 and going in minor 3rds:

4ths and major 3rds in diminshed scale steps alternating

4ths in minor thirds

It was my rare pleasure to jam with B.B. King during his encore at the Montreux Jazz Festival in July 2004. This pic was snapped backstage right afterwards!

73

Again, to make a 5th in the diminished scale, one must start with the note a half step below the tonic (in this case, B). The 5th and minor 6th combination can make for some interesting effects:

5ths and minor 6ths in diminished scale steps

5ths and minor 6ths in diminished scale steps alternating

The perfect 5th must be moved around in minor 3rds, tritones, or major 6ths, and always from the half step below:

5ths in minor thirds

5ths in minor thirds alternating

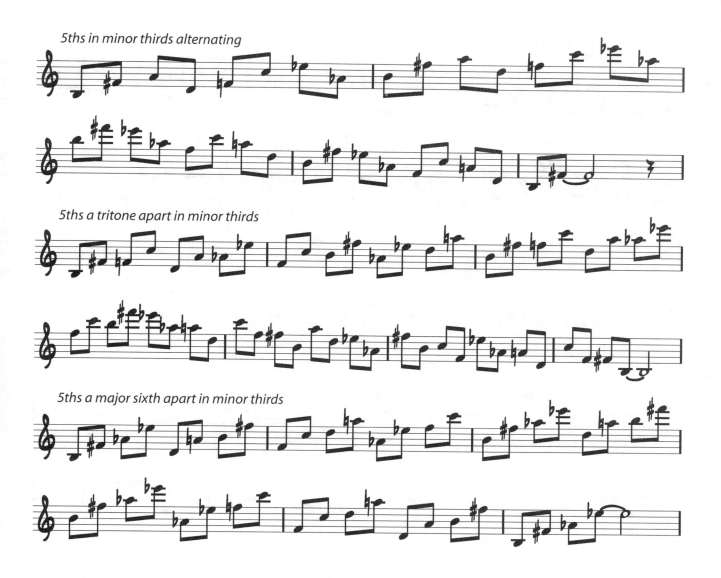

5ths a tritone apart in minor thirds

5ths a major sixth apart in minor thirds

You can also use chromatic approaches when playing your perfect 5ths through the diminished scale, from above on the lower note, and below on the upper note:

5ths in minor thirds w/lower chromatic approach

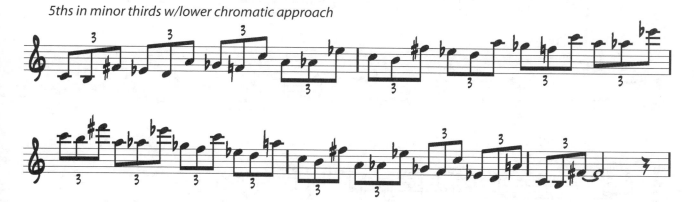

76

5ths in minor thirds w/upper chromatic approach

5ths in minor thirds w/dual chromatic approach

5ths in minor thirds reversed w/dual chromatic approach

As the 5th resolves to a minor 6th in the diminished scale, so does the minor 6th resolve to a 5th:

Minor 6ths and 5ths in diminished scale steps

Minor 6ths and 5ths in diminished scale steps alternating

And the minor 6th played in minor 3rds is a particularly nice bit of melodic material:

Minor 6ths in minor thirds

Béla Bartók used variations of this one in his Violin Concerto:

Minor 6ths in minor thirds alternating

Minor 6ths in minor thirds w/chromatic approach

This one could also be analyzed as a spread D7b5 (or G#7b5) arpeggio, in minor 3rds:

Minor 6ths a tritone apart in minor thirds

Minor 6ths a tritone apart in minor thirds alternating

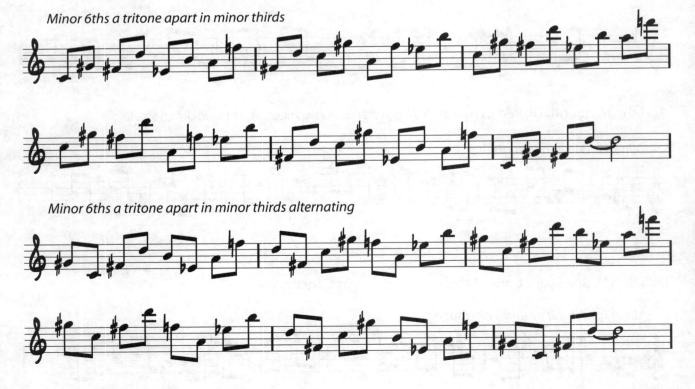

Now, on to the major 6th...another of the intervals contained in the basic diminished 7th chord... so it can be moved through the scale steps without any changes:

Major 6ths in diminished scale steps

Major 6ths in diminished scale steps alternating

Major 6ths in diminished scale steps broken

The major 6th also works well with the chromatic approach from below:

Major 6ths in minor thirds w/chromatic approach

Or the whole tone approach from above:

Major 6ths in minor thirds w/upper whole tone approach

Or various combinations of the two:

Major 6ths in minor thirds w/upper and lower approach

Major 6ths in minor thirds w/dual lower approach

Major 6ths in minor thirds w/dual upper approach

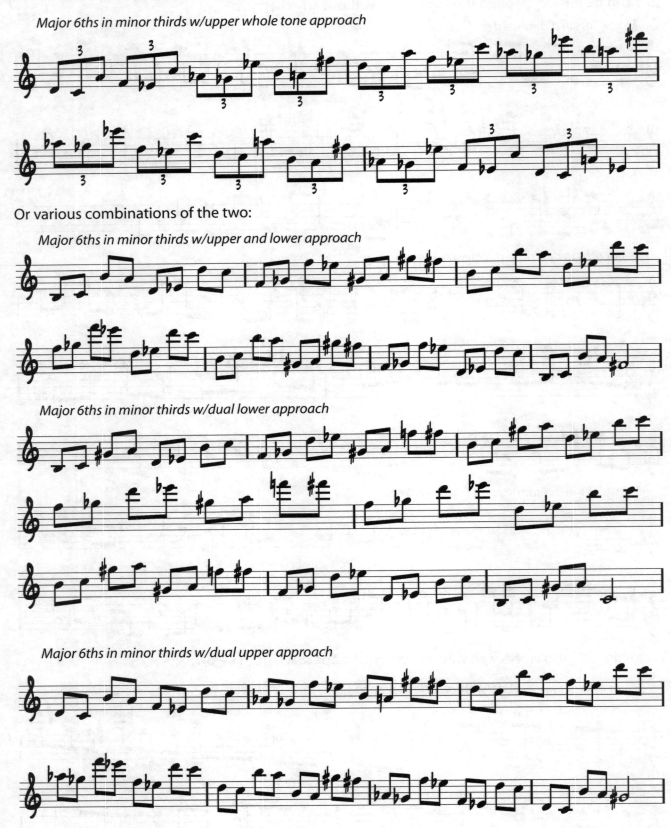

And now we come to the minor 7th...another of the intervals available only from the secondary scale tones. The combination of minor and major 7ths we get from moving this interval up the scale is very 20th century sounding!

Minor 7ths and major 7ths in diminished scale steps

Minor 7ths and major 7ths in diminished scale steps alternating

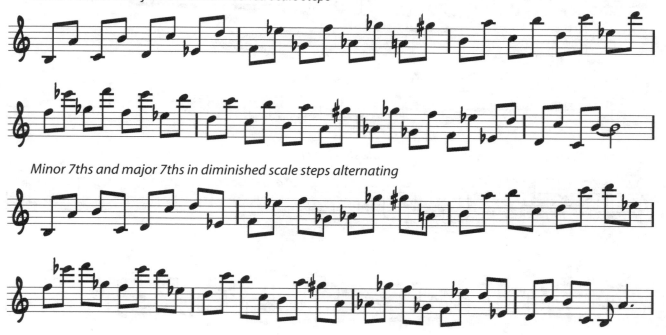

The minor 7th moved around in minor 3rds is kind of a strange sound, but I am including a few things with it anyway. Remember: the object is to get every possible combination of notes comfortably under your fingers!

Minor 7ths in minor thirds

Minor 7ths in minor thirds alternating

Minor 7ths in minor thirds w/dual lower approach

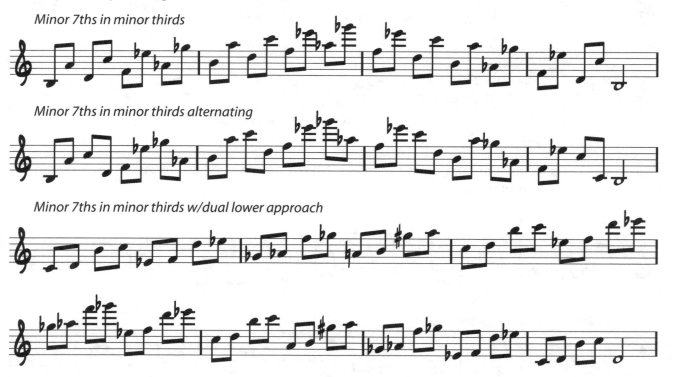

Major 7ths and minor 7ths in diminished scale steps

Major 7ths and minor 7ths in diminished scale steps alternating

Major 7ths and minor 7ths in diminished scale steps alternating reversed

The major 7th is more adaptable than the minor 7th to being moved around in minor 3rds...and can produce some wild melodic effects!

Major 7ths in minor thirds

Major 7ths in minor thirds alternating

Major 7ths in minor thirds reversed

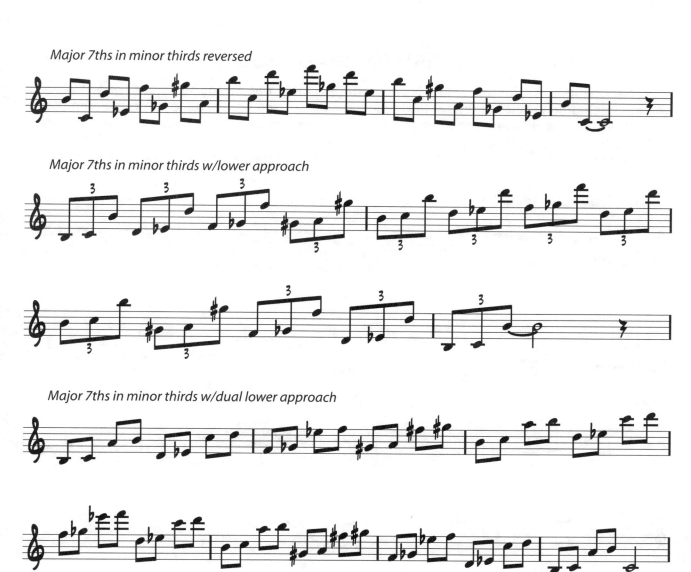

Major 7ths in minor thirds w/lower approach

Major 7ths in minor thirds w/dual lower approach

And, finally, one of my personal favorites:

Major 7ths a tritone apart, reversed and alternating, in minor thirds

DIMINISHED TRIAD STUDIES

Well, that about does it for our 2-note interval studies within the diminished scale. I hope everyone has been doing their homework and practicing these exercises on the other two diminished scales! For those who haven't, go ahead...take a few weeks, go back and review! Because there is a LOT more melodic material ahead of us. Now comes the moment you have been waiting for.... now, we get to play... 3-NOTE GROUPS!! Yes, triads are a lot of fun in the diminished scale...here goes:

Diminished triad 3's in scale steps

Diminished triad 3's in scale steps alternating

There are a lot of things you can do with the basic diminished triad, since it can be played through the steps of the scale. But not all of the possibilities are that melodically fulfilling. We will just list some of them here. But you can turn them up, down, around, any way you like, and run them up the scale. If you think of some more variations that aesthetically satisfy you, feel free to practice away!

Diminished triad 4's in scale steps

Diminished triad 1st inversion 3's

86

Diminished triad 1st inversion 3's reversed alternating

Diminished triad 1st inversion 4's

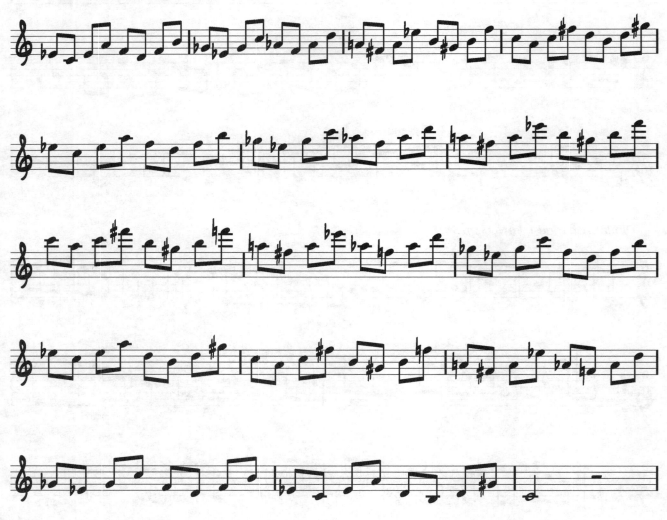

Diminished triad 2nd inversion 3's

Diminished triad 2nd inversion 3's reversed

Diminished triad 2nd inversion 3's alternating

Diminished triad 2nd inversion 4's broken

And here is a particularly nice one:

Diminished triad 1st inversion going up, 2nd inversion going down (triplets written in 4)

The diminished triad can also be moved around in minor 3rds with chromatic approaches on any of the notes. Needless to say, this is another way to outline the diminished 7th arpeggio.

Diminished triads in minor thirds w/chromatic approach

Diminished triads in minor thirds reversed w/chromatic approach

Diminished triads 1st inversion in minor thirds w/chromatic approach

90

Diminished triads 1st inversion in minor thirds w/chromatic approach on middle note

Diminished triads 1st inversion in minor thirds w/chromatic approach on upper note

Diminished triads 1st inversion in minor thirds reversed w/chromatic approach

Diminished triads 2nd inversion in minor thirds broken w/chromatic approach

Diminished triads 2nd inversion in minor thirds reversed w/chromatic approach

Diminished triads 2nd inversion in minor thirds broken w/chromatic approach on middle note

You can go on forever with this stuff:

*Diminished triads 2nd inversion broken in minor thirds w/chromatic approach on every note
(6 note pattern)*

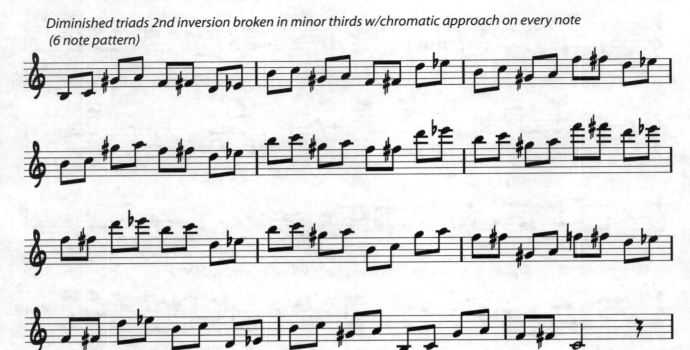

But the great thing about the diminished scale is that it contains so many other kinds of triads, including major, minor, and certain quartal triads. And these can all be moved around melodically in minor 3rds. In fact, ANY combination of notes made from the diminished scale will transpose cleanly in increments of minor 3rds. Or tritones. The modern jazz soloist will make good use of this convenient fact. Remember: all diminished triads can be the 3rd, 5th, and 7th of a dominant 7th chord whose root is one of the secondary scale tones. Go back and analyze the diminished triad studies in minor 3rds...you will see the 3rd, 5th, and 7th of B7, D7, F7, and Ab(G#)7. And those are the tonal centers to be aware of within this particular scale. You can see them very easily in our first diminished scale major triad exercise:

Major triads in minor 3rds

Four distinct major triads within every diminished scale! You can do a lot of things with them
and their various inversions:

Major triads in minor 3rds alternating

Major triads in minor 3rds in 4's

Major triads in minor 3rds broken in 4's

94

Major triads 1st inversion in minor 3rds reversed

Major triads 1st inversion in minor 3rds in 4's

Major triads 2nd inversion in minor 3rds (reversed descending)

Major triads 2nd inversion in minor 3rds alternating

Major triads 2nd inversion in minor 3rds in 4's

Clearly, there are a lot more mathematical possibilities for playing these triads in minor 3rds, inverting them, starting from different notes and so on, but we do not need to list them all here. If you think of one that you like, go ahead and practice it! Right now I would like to point out that major triads will also melodize nicely when combined with a triad a tritone away:

It's the old b5 substitution effect. And of course, since the two triads both come from the diminished scale, any note groups made from combining them can also be moved around in minor 3rds! This makes for a wealth of very hip sounding melodic material:

Major triads a tritone apart in minor 3rds alternating

96

Major triads a tritone apart in minor 3rds reversed alternating

Or you can just use the basic two triads a tritone apart, going from one to the other, through all their inversions:

Major triads a tritone apart alternating

Major triads a tritone apart in 4's

Interestingly, since the diminished scale (in half step-whole step mode) contains both the major and minor third, you can also use minor triads in minor 3rd and tritone steps in the same way we just did the major triads:

Minor triads in minor 3rds alternating

Minor triads in minor 3rds in 4's

Minor triads 1st inversion in minor thirds (reversed on descent)

98

Minor triads 1st inversion in minor 3rds broken in 4's

Minor triads 2nd inversion in minor 3rds alternating

Minor triads 2nd inversion in minor 3rds in 4's

Minor triads a tritone apart in minor 3rds

DIMINISHED QUARTAL TRIADS

All right, enough of this minor triad stuff. Some of it is useful, and it is always a good thing to get as many variations as possible under your fingers, but a lot of it is really not that fantastic. However, QUARTAL triads through the diminished scale produce some really good and fresh melodic figures. The standard quartal triad (three 4ths) cannot be made from the diminished scale, but its two relatives, which contain a fourth and a tritone, work wonderfully. Consider the triad of C, F#, and B...a tritone and a 4th. It can be analyzed as a D13 chord (containing the 7th, 3rd and 6th) or an Ab7(#9)(3rd, 7th and #9). Either way, it relates to 2 of the 4 dominant 7th chords that are part of the scale, and can be used melodically on any of them.

Quartal triads in minor 3rds

Quartal triads in minor 3rds reversed

Quartal triads in minor 3rds alternating

Quartal triads in minor 3rds in 4's

Quartal triads in minor 3rds w/chromatic approach (4 note arpeggios)

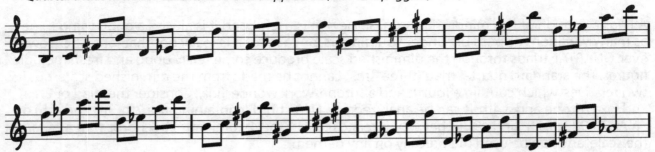

Try placing the accent on the 2nd note of these triplets...it's kind of like a little blues lick...7th to flat 3rd to major 3rd of their respective dominant 7th chords.

Quartal triads 1st inversion in minor 3rds

Quartal triads 1st inversion in minor 3rds reversed

Quartal triads 1st inversion in minor 3rds in 4's

This one was already covered in the diminished interval section as tritones in minor 3rds with chromatic approach. However, it can also be regarded as:

Quartal triads 2nd inversion in minor 3rds

Quartal triads 2nd inversion in minor 3rds reversed

Quartal triads 2nd inversion in minor 3rds in 4's

Quartal triads a major 6th apart in minor 3rds

102

The second type of quartal triad to come from the diminished scale is composed of a 4th with a tritone on top, rather than the other way around. It is interesting to analyze: C, F, and B, for example, could be a Dmi13, an Fma(#11), a G7 with an added 4th...lots of things, but for diminished soloing purposes, I prefer to think of it as the top 3 notes of a dominant 13(#9) chord...the C being the 3rd in Ab or the 7th in D, the F being the 13 in Ab or the #9 in D, and the B being the 13 in D or the #9 in Ab! That's not too confusing, is it?

Type 2 quartal triads in minor 3rds

Type 2 quartal triads in minor 3rds reversed

Type 2 quartal triads in minor 3rds alternating

Type 2 quartal triads in minor 3rds in 4's

Type 2 quartal triads in minor 3rds in 4's reversed

Again, this one was included in the interval section as 5ths in minor 3rds with upper chromatic approach, but here it has become:

Type 2 quartal triads 1st inversion in minor 3rds

Type 2 quartal triads 1st inversion in minor 3rds reversed

Type 2 quartal triads 1st inversion in minor 3rds in 4's

104

Type 2 quartal triads 2nd inversion in minor 3rds

Type 2 quartal triads 2nd inversion in minor 3rds reversed

Type 2 quartal triads 2nd inversion in minor 3rds in 4's

Type 2 quartal triads in minor 3rds w/chromatic approach (4 note arpeggios)

DIMINISHED 7th CHORD STUDIES

OK. It is time now to get into our 4-note groups from the diminished scale. A lot of these are used frequently by the best and most advanced soloists. Almost all of them will be played in minor 3rds, but let's start by remembering that the basic diminished 7th chord, and its partner a whole step above, do contain all the notes of the scale, and thus can be played in scale steps:

Diminished 7th chords in scale steps

Yes, it's always good to have that stuff under your fingers. Of course, there are a great number of possibilities for 4-note groups within this scale. But some of the best are slight alterations of the diminished 7th chord. For example, if you take the basic diminished 7th and extend the top note by one scale step, you get Example 1 below. If you extend the top 2 notes, Example 2.

Ex. 1   *Ex. 2*

Cdim7   Cdim7 (extended)   Cdim7   Cdim (double extended)

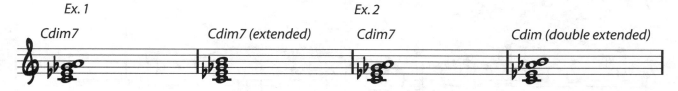

Now, you can look at the Cdim (extended) in a number of ways. It could be a B triad over C, an Ab7 with a #9 on top, or my personal favorite, D13(b9), as it contains the b7(C), 3(F#), b9(Eb) and 13(B). And the 13(b9) chord is peculiar to the diminished scale...it really embodies the uniqueness of a dominant 7th chord in diminished mode. And of course, you can play these patterns across any of the dominant 7th chords (B, D, F, Ab) built from the secondary scale tones of the C diminished scale.

Diminished 7th extended in minor 3rds

Diminished 7th extended in minor 3rds reversed

Diminished 7th extended in minor 3rds broken

Diminished 7th extended in minor 3rds irreparably broken

You can use the diminished (double extended) in the same way as in the previous examples. It is equally interesting to look at this chord form from a variety of angles to gain perspective on what the diminished scale really means. Cdim (double extended), for example, can be an Ab triad with a minor 3rd (or minor with a major 3rd!), a B13(b9) without the 7th, F7(b5#9) (with a 5th), or D13(b5b9)!

Diminished 7th double extended in minor 3rds

Diminished 7th double extended in minor 3rds reversed

Diminished 7th double extended in minor 3rds broken

Diminished 7th double extended in minor 3rds seriously messed with

108

There are a ton of cool 4-note combinations from the diminished scale that can be played in minor 3rds. Many are variations on the dim7th extensions. Practice them, transpose them to the other two diminished scales, use them in good health!

4ths a tritone apart in minor 3rds

4ths in minor 3rds w/dual chromatic approach (an inversion of the previous exercise)

C diminished extended spread voicing in minor 3rds

Dominant 7th chords in minor 3rds

Dominant 7th chords in minor 3rds broken

Dominant 7th flat 5 chords in minor 3rds

Tritones a major 7th apart in minor 3rds (13#9 chords)

Tritones a major 7th apart in minor 3rds (13#9 chords) alternating

If you look at this next group as starting from the 7th and major 3rd, they are:

7b5(13) chords in minor 3rds

7b5(13) chords in minor 3rds broken

Minor 6ths a major 6th apart in minor 3rds

Minor 6ths a major 6th apart in minor 3rds reversed

I think you are getting the idea by now. ANY possible combination of notes from the diminished scale can be grouped together as melodic sections and moved around in the diminished chord intervals of minor 3rds, tritones, and major 6ths. There is no way I could have included ALL the possible combinations here, but I think you have plenty to work with...and work on! Don't forget to transpose and practice as much as you can in the other two diminished scales! Before we move on, here are a couple more scale exercises that I saved until now for a special moment such as this:

Diminished scale broken half steps

Diminished scale broken half steps reversed

Diminished scale broken whole steps

And one more for good measure:

Blues lick in minor thirds

There are plenty of opportunities and musical situations for the modern jazz soloist to delve into his diminished scale repertoire! In an older style, it could be on a straight diminished chord, such as here in the second 8 bars of "Mack The Knife" – **CD TRACK #11**

Or in a more modern tune such as Herbie Hancock's "Dolphin Dance". There is a very tasty diminished (double extended) chord in the last 4 bar turnaround – **CD TRACK #12**

But again, probably the most valuable use of the diminished scale is to stretch the tonality of the dominant 7th chord. As I mentioned earlier, diminished stuff will work on any alteration of the dominant 7th except the 7(#5), because the scale contains the b9, #9, b5, and 5. But since it also has the natural 6th (13), the 13(b9) and 13(#9) chords are the ones that really embody the true diminished flavor! – **CD TRACK #13**

Section 6 - The Chromatic Scale

And now, at last, we arrive at the final frontier in our exploration of melodic materials: the chromatic scale. Where there are no rules, and every possible combination of notes is permitted. But there is a systematic approach to mastering this all-encompassing scale. The intervals and note groups must be studied one at a time, focusing on the melodic strength of their shapes, in the combinations that are not possible with any other scale source. The modern jazz soloist will understand that the chromatic scale gives him instant access to play "outside" whatever harmonic background is present, with his access back "inside" that harmony never more than a half step away! Think about that.

And here is the good news: your chromatic scale exercises will not have to be transposed and practiced in any other keys....because, there IS no other key!

We start with one of the most valuable of all the studies, the major 2nds. I use them all the time, and if you listen to Miles Davis you will hear him using them a lot too, especially in his faster licks. They are a fabulous connector between all kinds of stuff and should be thoroughly learned.

═══ CHROMATIC INTERVAL STUDIES ═══

Chromatic major 2nds

These next variations will be written out in just one octave, to save space. Obviously, they should be practiced through the range of your instrument.

Chromatic major 2nds alternating

114

Chromatic major 2nds two up, one down and vice versa

Now, this one could be a straight chromatic scale exercise, but within this particular context it should be regarded as:

Chromatic major 2nds alternating w/chromatic connections

Minor 3rds are also a very handy melodic device when used chromatically. They remind you of diminished, but have their own distinct flavor.

Chromatic minor 3rds

Chromatic minor 3rds alternating

Chromatic minor 3rds (triplets)

And now, another chromatic scale exercise masquerading as...

Chromatic minor 3rds alternating w/chromatic connections

Chromatic major 3rds

Chromatic major 3rds alternating

Chromatic major 3rds (reversed triplets)

The fourth works well in chromatic mode, as does its inversion, the fifth. They form the foundation of a lot of chords, and I believe that this gives them a certain power and melodic strength.

Chromatic 4ths

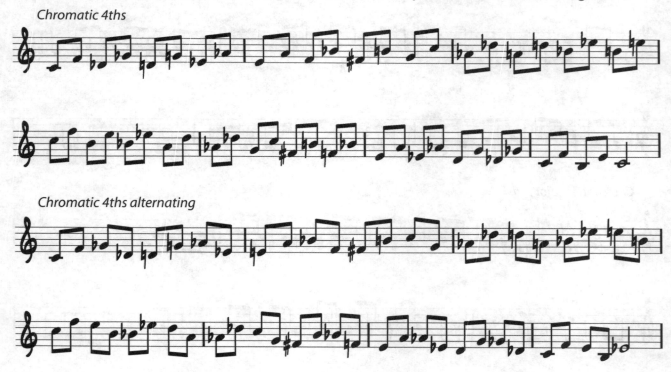

Chromatic 4ths alternating

Chromatic 4ths, 2 up one down and vice versa

Chromatic 4ths (reversed triplets)

Chromatic tritones

Chromatic tritones alternating

118

Chromatic tritones (triplets)

Chromatic 5ths

Chromatic 5ths alternating

Chromatic 5ths (triplets)

The wider intervals such as the minor and major 6ths start to get melodically interesting when played in chromatic mode.

Chromatic minor 6ths

Chromatic minor 6ths alternating

Chromatic minor 6ths, 2 up one down

Chromatic minor 6ths (triplets)

Chromatic minor 6ths (reversed triplets)

Chromatic major 6ths

Chromatic major 6ths alternating

These next two sound kind of like endless country and western intros!

Chromatic major 6ths (triplets)

Chromatic major 6ths (reversed triplets)

Chromatic minor 7ths

Chromatic minor 7ths (reversed)

Chromatic minor 7ths alternating

122

Chromatic major 7ths

Chromatic major 7ths reversed

Chromatic major 7ths alternating

Chromatic major 7ths (alternating triplets)

The chromatic scale exercises and patterns have two main purposes for the modern jazz soloist: First, to complete the task of mastering one's instrument by learning all the possible note combinations that were not covered in the study of the other scales. Second, and equally important, is to develop the ability to play INSIDE OR OUTSIDE the prevailing harmony with equal command. Since any of the chromatic patterns will, by definition, be OUTSIDE, the question becomes how to best integrate them with the inside stuff. The modern jazz soloist has a LOT of choices available here. Let's make good ones! You can start in a particular mode and use a chromatic bit to take it out and then back in. – **CD TRACK #14**

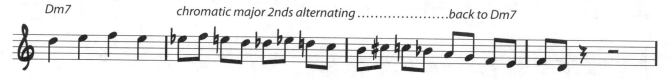

It is important to have a departure point and a re-entry point that make musical sense. Then you can get away with more adventurous stuff!

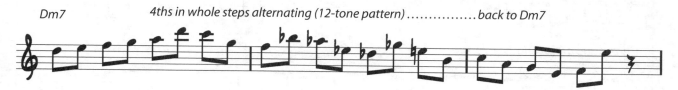

If you know exactly where you are in relation to the key you are in, the chromatic scale becomes your best friend!

If you are headed for a particular chord, aim your chromatic bit so that it will resolve to one of the chord tones. The end will justify the means!

CHROMATIC TRIAD STUDIES

Remember: our goal is to get as many note combinations as possible safely under our fingers. So it is a good idea to practice all our simple chord forms through the chromatic scale as well. I will not list EVERY possible permutation here, just enough to keep everybody honest!

Chromatic major triads 1st inversion in 4's

Chromatic major triads 2nd inversion alternating

Chromatic major triads 2nd inversion reversed

Chromatic major triads 2nd inversion 4 note groups alternating

Chromatic minor triads reversed alternating

Chromatic minor triads broken 4's

Chromatic minor triads 1st inversion reversed

Chromatic minor triads 1st inversion 4's

Chromatic minor triads 2nd inversion reversed

Chromatic minor triads 2nd inversion 4 note groups alternating

This shot was snapped by drummer Al Foster at the "Man With The Horn" sessions in CBS Studios, early 1981.

CHROMATIC QUARTAL TRIADS

The quartal triads have a multitude of uses throughout the chromatic scale. So let's make sure we have them solidly embedded in our muscle memory!

Chromatic quartal triads

Chromatic quartal triads reversed

Chromatic quartal triads alternating

130

Chromatic quartal triads 1st inversion reversed

Chromatic quartal triads 1st inversion 4 note groups alternating

Chromatic quartal triads 2nd inversion

Chromatic quartal triads 2nd inversion 4 note groups

Chromatic quartal triads (tritone-fourth)

Chromatic quartal triads (tritone-fourth) reversed

CHROMATIC DIMINISHED TRIADS

And, let's not forget our little diminished friends....

Chromatic diminished triads

Chromatic diminished triads reversed

Chromatic diminished triads 1st inversion

Chromatic diminished triads 2nd inversion reversed

The chromatic augmented triads are of particular interest because they comprise a twelve-tone sequence...a subject we will get into shortly.

Chromatic augmented triads alternating

CHROMATIC PENTATONIC BITS

4-note segments of the pentatonic scale are also very handy bits that the modern jazz soloist can put to good use by moving them through the chromatic scale. Especially guitar players! These little 4-note "boxes" can be turned around every which way. But caution: use them wisely!

Chromatic pentatonic bit

Chromatic pentatonic bit reversed

Chromatic pentatonic bit turned around every which way

And while we are on the subject of pentatonic bits, you might also try:

Chromatic minor pentatonic bit (reversed descending)

Chromatic major pentatonic bit

Or this lightning-fast passage (homage to Mike Brecker):

Chromatic pentatonic 6

CHROMATIC 7th CHORD STUDIES

And, of course, there are all the 4-note chord forms that can be run chromatically as well, in all their inversions and permutations if you have the patience for it! Here are just a few examples:

Chromatic major 7th chords

Chromatic major 7th chords alternating

Chromatic minor 7th chords (also a pentatonic bit)

Chromatic minor 7th chords (also a pentatonic bit) reversed descending

Chromatic dominant 7th chords 1st inversion

Chromatic dominant 7th(b5) chords

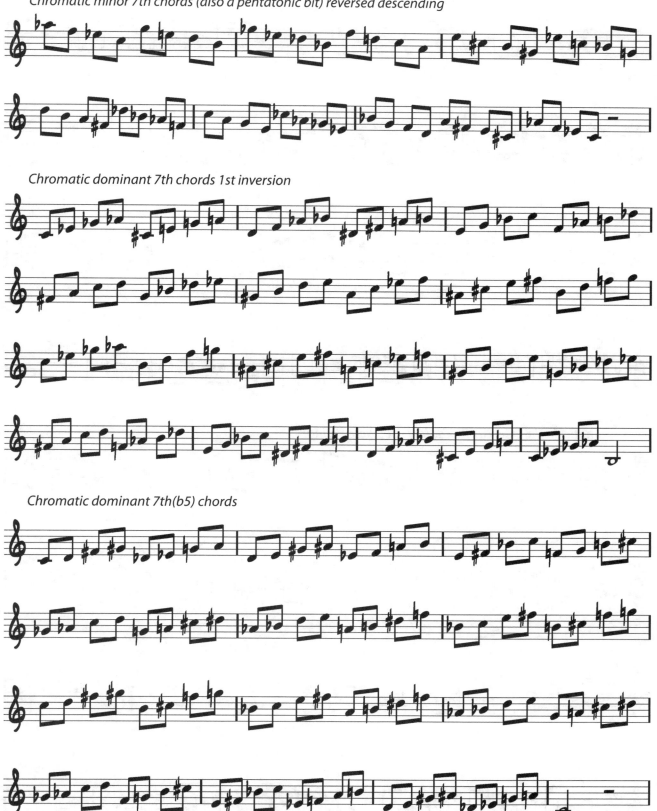

138

Chromatic major 7th(#5) chords alternating

Chromatic diminished 7th chords (reversed descending)

CHROMATIC 12-TONE STUDIES

The chromatic diminished 7th chords in the previous exercise also make up a 12-tone pattern. "12-tone" means that all of the notes in the chromatic scale are played before any of them are repeated. There are several very interesting ways to make 12-tone patterns which give insight into the mathematical nature of the structure of music. For instance, a 12-tone pattern can be made from the 3 diminished 7th chords:

Or the 4 augmented triads:

Or the circle of 4ths and 5ths
(up a 4th, down a 5th and/or vice versa ad infinitum):

Or the combination of the two 6-note whole tone scales
(each one of which contains 2 augmented triads):

You can see that there is an almost endless array of 12-tone patterns and permutations possible by using the above combinations. Some of them can be put to good use by the modern jazz soloist. Others, not so much. But the 12-tone concept can open the door to a lot of cool interval combinations that one will not be able to find in any other scale but the chromatic!

12-TONE INTERVAL STUDIES

Minor 3rds in whole steps

Minor 3rds in whole steps alternating

4ths in whole steps

4ths in whole steps alternating

5ths in whole steps

5ths in whole steps alternating

Major 6ths in whole steps

Major 6ths in whole steps alternating

Major 7ths in whole steps

Major 7ths in whole steps alternating

12-TONE TRIAD STUDIES

If you look at the last group of interval studies, you will see that the bottom notes of each interval make up one whole tone scale, and the top notes make up the other. So if you continue playing them up the whole tone ladder, you get a 12-tone group. Moving now to augmented triads, there are many ways to play them:

Augmented triads in minor 3rds

Augmented triads in minor 3rds reversed

Augmented triads in minor 3rds alternating

Augmented triads in minor 3rds broken (in 4)

The spread augmented voicing 12-tone pattern is also nice:

Augmented triads spread voicing in minor 3rds

But because of the symmetrical qualities of the augmented chords, you can do all kinds of things and still keep it a 12-tone pattern:

Augmented triads up a minor 3rd, down a half step, reversed

You can also play them in 4ths:

Augmented triads in 4ths, reversed descending

Or spread them out in 4ths:

Augmented triads spread voicing in 4ths

12-TONE 7th CHORD STUDIES

Interestingly, just as 4 augmented triads in minor 3rds or 4ths make a 12-tone pattern, so do 3 diminished 7th chords in major 2nds, 3rds, 4ths or 5ths! This makes for a large amount of 12-tone melodic material. Here are some examples:

Diminished 7th chords in whole steps (alternating on descent)

Diminished 7th chords in whole steps broken and reversed

Diminished 7th chords spread voicing in whole steps broken (tritones a major 6th apart)

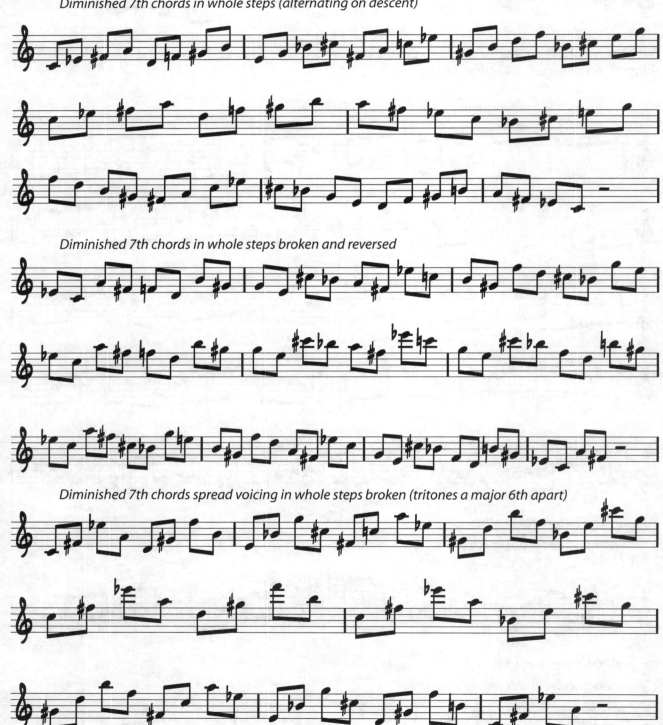

Diminished 7th chords spread voicing in whole steps broken (major 6ths a tritone apart)

Just as the dim7th chords ascending in whole steps are an inversion of the same chords descending chromatically, when they go up in major 3rds they are an inversion of the same chords ASCENDING chromatically!

Diminished 7th chords in major 3rds (reversed descending)

Diminished 7th chords spread voicing in major 3rds broken and reversed

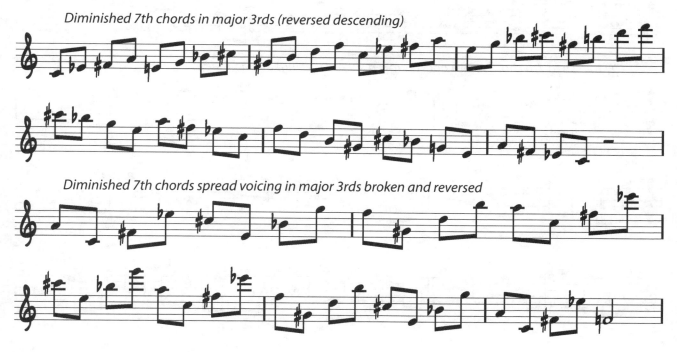

When you play them in 4ths (as in whole steps), you can hear those dominant 7th chords resolving chromatically downward (or in 4ths of course):

Diminished 7th chords in 4ths (reversed descending)

146

Diminished 7th chords in 4ths broken

Diminished 7th chords in 4ths broken and reversed

Diminished 7th chords a 5th apart (broken spread voicing) in whole steps

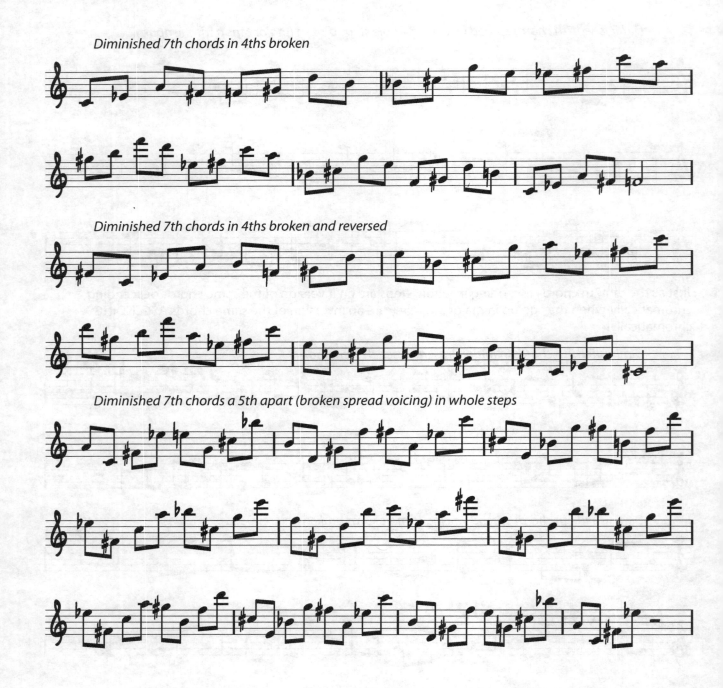

12-TONE CIRCLE OF FOURTHS & FIFTHS STUDIES

You can see that there are a ton of possible diminished 12-tone patterns... more than enough to satisfy the melodic cravings of even the most demanding modern jazz soloist! But now we turn our attention to the circle of 4ths and 5ths. These next 2 examples will be written as repeats:

Up two 4ths, down a 5th (down two 4ths, up a 5th descending)

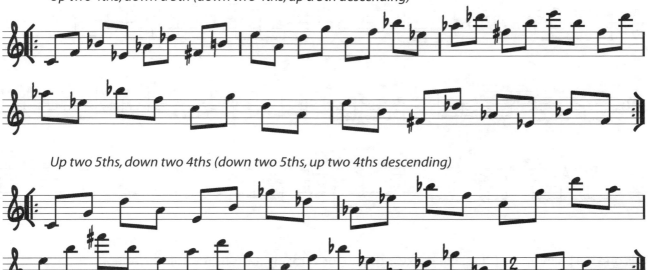

Up two 5ths, down two 4ths (down two 5ths, up two 4ths descending)

You can make endless circles of 4ths and 5ths. And the intervals themselves connect to each other so well, you almost don't notice that you are playing a 12-tone chromatic pattern! Check out the cool 5-note pattern that descends chromatically on this one:

4ths and 5ths (you figure it out!)

148

5ths and 4ths chromatically ascending 7-note group

This one is a palindrome (the same backwards and forwards). It starts its retrograde motion at the high D, 3rd note of bar 8.

Three 4ths up, two 5ths down (three 4ths down, two 5ths up descending)

DISPLACED CHROMATIC SCALE STUDIES

Another way to make a wild sounding 12-tone sequence is to simply play the chromatic scale, but displacing the notes by an octave. This gives you a combination of b9ths and major 7ths:

Displaced chromatic scale

Or you can always add that odd half step:

Displaced chromatic scale alternating

This is one of my personal favorites. It is based on a continually descending chromatic scale:

Displaced chromatic scale descending

You can also vary the number of straight chromatic notes between jumps:

Displaced chromatic scale descending (2 half steps)

150

Displaced chromatic scale descending (3 half steps)

And you can make a 12-tone group by simply taking segments of the chromatic scale and breaking them up into different sized groups:

Chromatic scale alternating 4 note groups

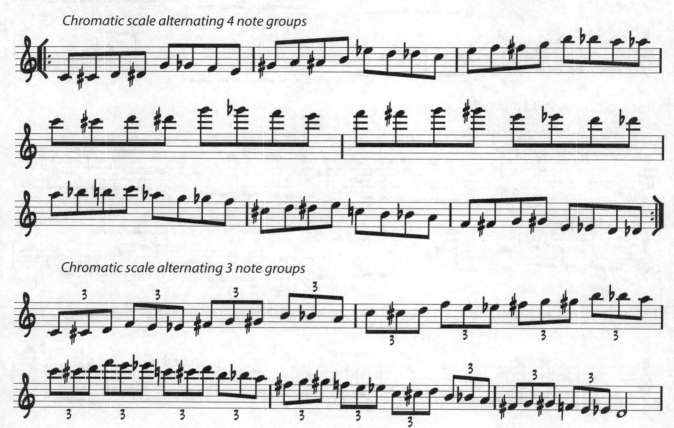

Chromatic scale alternating 3 note groups

You can then change the order of the notes within those groups. Remember the major 2nds that began the chromatic section?

Groups of 2 chromatic major 2nds a major 3rd apart

Groups of 2 chromatic major 2nds alternating a major 3rd apart

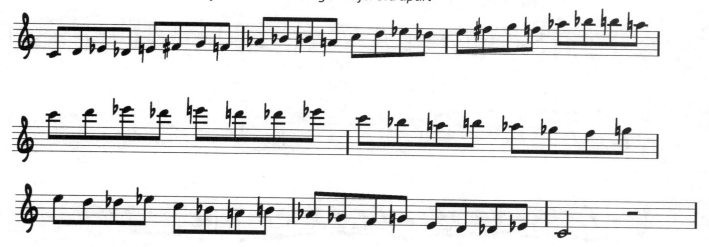

That should be enough 12-tone material for our present purposes. Although I am sure you can see there is PLENTY more available! The modern jazz soloist is always searching for new licks to add to his repertoire, and the chromatic ocean is a good place to fish! And while we are on the subject of major 2nds again, these little segments of the whole tone scale make very nifty chromatic riffs:

Chromatic 3 note whole tone scale segments alternating

Chromatic 4-note whole tone scale segments alternating

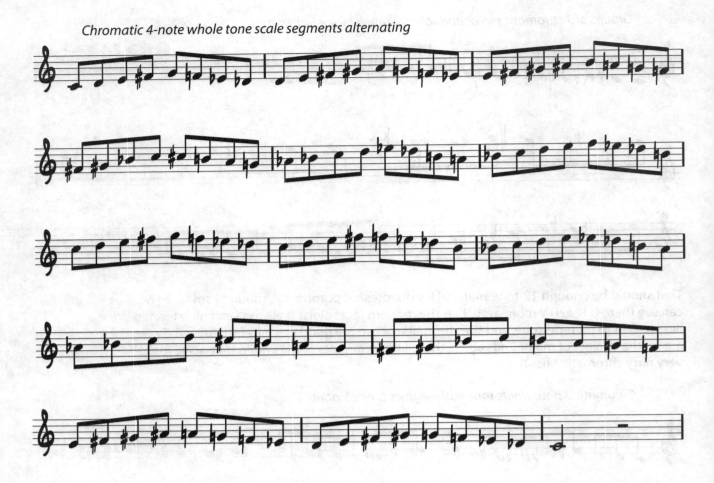

This, then, is the essence of making melodic materials from the chromatic scale: pick a note group, and move it around symmetrically in any interval distance that you choose. Invert, rotate, reverse, and/or alternate the notes in your note group. Move it around again. There are no rules, no right and wrong notes. The only thing that counts is the musicality of your choices.

4-note group (BCEF) in whole steps

Reversed (FECB) in whole steps

Reversed and inverted (CBFE) in whole steps

Rotated (FBCE) in whole steps

Rotated and reversed (BFEC) in whole steps

I hope and believe that the exercises in this book, if studied correctly, will improve the overall musicianship and expand the improvisational abilities of anyone aspiring to be a better modern jazz soloist. Don't forget: these are just the raw materials. The inspiration, the creativity, and (let us not forget) the HOMEWORK(!) are up to you. We will finish with just a few more little ideas for riffs that are emphatically chromatic!

Major 7(b5) chords spread voicing in whole steps (alternating on descent)

13th chords w/chromatic approach from (way!) above, in whole steps

Major 7ths a tritone apart, alternating in major 3rds

Finally, a little phrase to meditate on, containing all the intervals in sequence:

Intervals expanding and contracting chromatically

I played the Inauguration on Jan. 20, 1989, with the Bob Hardwick Society Orchestra. The President personally autographed one of these for me. It hangs on my wall to this day. Not to imply that I would have voted for that elitist old Republican S.O.B., or his kid either!

Appendix

Another good source of melodic material is to take a three or four note group and play it up and down your instrument as an arpeggio, then break it down into sections in 3's and 4's. (You will want to transpose these!)

3 octave pentatonic bit

3 octave pentatonic bit in triplets

3 octave slightly spread pentatonic bit

3 octave slightly spread pentatonic bit played in 4's

And don't forget, you can take any one of these little groups and move them around in any interval distances that you might find aesthetically satisfying!

Slightly spread pentatonic bit in minor 3rds

Slightly spread pentatonic bit in whole steps (reversed descending)

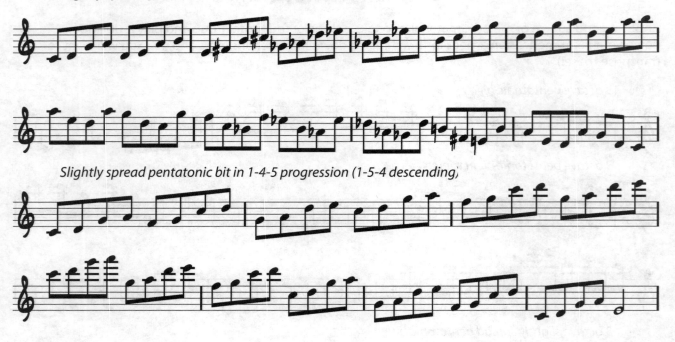

Slightly spread pentatonic bit in 1-4-5 progression (1-5-4 descending)

The possibilities really are never-ending!

Quartal triads 1st inversion ascending in major 3rds, descending in 4ths

4th a half step apart (B-E, C-F) arpeggio descending 1/2 step higher

4th a half step apart (B-E, C-F) arpeggio in 4's

Another very handy melodic device is what I call the "pivot". The soloist simply pivots off one note or group of notes to the other notes of the scale... whichever one he happens to be playing at the time! The notes can go up from the pivot:

Pivoting up from C

Or down:

Pivoting down from C

The pivot is useful through the modes as well. Here is an example in Dorian mode with a 2-note lead-in (C-D)

Pivoting from C-D in Dorian mode

Pivoting off a 3-note group is a little reminiscent of Bach!

Pivoting from C-B-C up and down

Of course, you can also pivot through the other scales:

Whole tone pivot

Diminished pivot

Chromatic pivot

And the pivot is a good way to outline different chords as well:

C major   F minor

C minor   D dom. 7th

G dom.7th

I want to say a few words here about one of the most valuable of all materials for the modern jazz soloist: the melodic minor scale. I did not think it necessary to devote an entire section to it earlier because it is so similar to the major scale; C melodic minor, for example, is simply a C major scale with a flat 3rd.

C melodic minor

Therefore, the melodic minor scales can be practiced in exactly the same way as the diatonic scales, through all the same scale, interval and note group patterns that are found on pages 1-34. Go over them in all 12 keys, making sure, of course, to flat the 3rd!

C melodic minor thirds alternating, etc. etc. etc.

The 7th chord extensions of the melodic minor scale are interesting:

But the melodic minor scale is much more than the scale of choice for soloing on the minor (major 7th) chord and its upper extension, the major 7th(#5). Two of its most unique and valuable qualities are revealed in its fourth mode (the lydian dominant scale) and its seventh mode (known in the jazz world as the altered scale)!

F lydian dominant (F7 with 9,#11, and 13)   B altered (B7 with flat and sharp 9s and 5s)

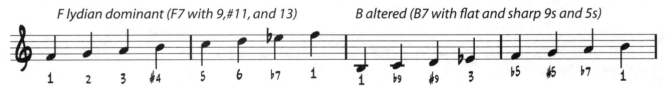

So whenever you see a dominant 7th chord with a NATURAL 9th and/or 13th and you want to add the color of the #11(#4), the lydian dominant mode of the melodic minor scale is for you! When the dominant 7th chord contains any of the combinations of b5, #5, b9 and/or #9 (but no 13th!), then it is the altered scale, the mode of the melodic minor scale starting from the seventh note, that becomes the preferred vehicle of expression for the discriminating modern jazz soloist!

B7(+9,+5) (or F7#11)

I would also like to offer a few ideas here on a VERY big subject: motif development. A "motif" is defined in the dictionary as: "a theme that is elaborated on in a piece of music" or "a short succession of notes producing a single impression; a brief melodic or rhythmic formula out of which longer passages are developed".

It is extremely important for the modern jazz soloist to be aware of various ways to MAKE MOTIFS out of the various melodic materials presented here and DEVELOP THEM! There are so many ways to do this, and the limits are bounded only by your own creativity!

For example, let us take one of the simplest of possible motifs: a broken C major triad:

If we use that rhythm (quarter note-two eighth notes-two beat rest) and that melody, we can develop it up the scale:

We can use the same rhythm, the same scale, but with a one beat rest:

Or if we go back to the first phrase, but choose not to stay within that particular key, we can take it through the circle of 4ths:

Still using the same basic phrase, we can vary the rhythms, the order of the notes, and the interval distance between them any way we like:

We can reverse the rhythms and note orders as we play with the space between phrases:

Or we can make it a rhythmic motif ONLY, and change the notes any which way, while the rhythm remains the same:

So, motifs can be melodic and/or rhythmic figures. They can be thematic "nuggets", the basic musical reference points that hold a solo together. They can be connected by various other melodic materials, but they will stand out in the overall scheme:

There are endless ways to develop motifs. They do not always have to be repeated exactly. Sometimes they can be inverted, extended, extrapolated upon...as long as you do it in a musical manner, the choices are up to you!

Check out **CD TRACK #15** and **#16** here.

The next book in this series will be entitled "Harmonic Possibilities of the Improvised Line." In it I look forward to exploring the melodic possibilities available to the modern jazz soloist through the exploration of harmonic materials. I leave you now with one small example:

Harmonic etude (playing with circle of 4ths)

The Real Easy Book Vol. 1
TUNES FOR BEGINNING IMPROVISERS

Published by Sher Music Co. in conjunction with
the Stanford Jazz Workshop. $22 list price.

The easiest tunes from Horace Silver, Eddie Harris,
Freddie Hubbard, Red Garland, Sonny Rollins, Cedar
Walton, Wes Montgomery Cannonball Adderly, etc.
Get yourself or your beginning jazz combo sound-
ing good right away with the first fake book ever
designed for the beginning improviser.
Available in C, Bb, Eb and Bass Clef.

The Real Easy Book Vol. 2
TUNES FOR INTERMEDIATE IMPROVISER

Published by Sher Music Co. in conjunction with
the Stanford Jazz Workshop. Over 240 pages. $29.

The best intermediate-level tunes by: Charlie Parker,
John Coltrane, Miles Davis, John Scofield, Sonny Rollins
Horace Silver, Wes Montgomery, Freddie Hubbard,
Cal Tjader, Cannonball Adderly, and more!
Both volumes feature instructional material tailored for
each tune. Perfect for jazz combos!
Available in C, Bb, Eb and Bass Clef.

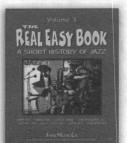

The Real Easy Book Vol. 3
A SHORT HISTORY OF JAZZ

Published by Sher Music Co. in conjunction with
the Stanford Jazz Workshop. Over 200 pages. $25.

History text and tunes from all eras and styles of jazz.
Perfect for classroom use. Available in C, Bb, Eb
and Bass Clef versions.

The Best of Sher Music Co
Real Books
100+ TUNES YOU NEED TO KNOW

A collection of the best-known songs from the world
leader in jazz fake books -- Sher Music Co.!

Includes songs by: Miles Davis, John Coltrane, Bill Evans
Duke Ellington, Antonio Carlos Jobim, Charlie Parker,
John Scofield, Michael Brecker, Weather Report, Horac
Silver, Freddie Hubbard, Thelonious Monk, Cannonball
Adderley, and many more!

$26. Available in C, Bb, Eb and Bass Clef.

The Serious Jazz Book II
THE HARMONIC APPROACH

By Barry Finnerty, Endorsed by: Joe Lovano,
Jamey Aebersold, Hubert Laws, Mark Levine, etc.

- A 200 page, exhaustive study of how to master
  the harmonic content of songs.
- Contains explanations of every possible type of
  chord that is used in jazz.
- Clear musical examples to help achieve real
  harmonic control over melodic improvisation.
- For any instrument. $32. Money back gurantee!

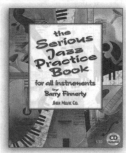

The Serious Jazz
Practice Book By Barry Finnerty

A unique and comprehensive plan for mastering
the basic building blocks of the jazz language.
It takes the most widely-used scales and chords
and gives you step-by-step exercises that dissect
them into hundreds of cool, useable patterns.
Includes CD - $30 list price.

"The book I've been waiting for!" – Randy Brecker.

"The best book of intervallic studies I've ever seen."
– Mark Levine

The Jazz Theory Book

By Mark Levine, the most comprehensive Jazz Theory
book ever published! $38 list price.

- Over 500 pages of text and over 750 musical
  examples.
- Written in the language of the working jazz musician, this book is easy to read and user-friendly.
  At the same time, it is the most comprehensive
  study of jazz harmony and theory ever published.
- Mark Levine has worked with Bobby Hutcherson,
  Cal Tjader, Joe Henderson, Woody Shaw, and
  many other jazz greats.

Jazz Piano Masterclass
With Mark Levine
"THE DROP 2 BOOK"

The long-awaited book from the author of
"The Jazz Piano Book!" A complete study on how to us
"drop 2" chord voicings to create jazz piano magic!
68 pages, plus CD of Mark demonstrating each exercise
$19 list.

"Will make you sound like a real jazz piano player
in no time." – Jamey Aebersold

Metaphors For
The Musician
By Randy Halberstadt

This practical and enlightening book will help any
jazz player or vocalist look at music with "new eyes."
Designed for any level of player, on any instrument,
"Metaphors For The Musician" provides numerous
exercises throughout to help the reader turn these
concepts into musical reality.

Guaranteed to help you improve your musicianship.
330 pages – $29 list price. Satisfaction guaranteed!

The Jazz Musicians Guide
To Creative Practicing
By David Berkman

Finally a book to help musicians use their practice
time wisely! Covers tune analysis, breaking hard
tunes into easy components, how to swing better,
tricks to playing fast bebop lines, and much more!
150+pages, plus CD. $29 list.

"Fun to read and bursting with things to do
and ponder." – Bob Mintzer

The 'Real Easy'
Ear Training Book
By Roberta Radley

For all musicians, regardless of instrument or experience,
this is the most comprehensive book on "hearing the
changes" ever published!

- Covers both beginning and intermediate ear training
  exercises.
- Music Teachers: You will find this book invaluable in
  teaching ear training to your students.

Book includes 168 pages of instructional text and
musical examples, plus two CDs! $29 list price.

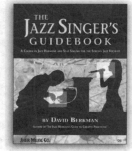

The Jazz Singer's
Guidebook By David Berkman
A COURSE IN JAZZ HARMONY AND SCAT SINGI
FOR THE SERIOUS JAZZ VOCALIST

A clear, step-by-step approach for serious singers who
want to improve their grasp of jazz harmony and gain a
deeper understanding of music fundamentals.

This book will change how you hear music and make yo
better singer, as well as give you the tools to develop y
singing in directions you may not have thought possible

$26 – includes audio CD demonstrating many exercises

The Latin Real Book (C, Bb or Eb)

The only professional-level Latin fake book ever published!
Over 570 pages. Detailed transcriptions exactly as recorded by:

Ray Barretto	Arsenio Rodriguez	Manny Oquendo	Ivan Lins
Eddie Palmieri	Tito Rodriguez	Puerto Rico All-Stars	Djavan
Fania All-Stars	Orquesta Aragon	Issac Delgaldo	Tom Jobim
Tito Puente	Beny Moré	Ft. Apache Band	Toninho Horta
Ruben Blades	Cal Tjader	Dave Valentin	Joao Bosco
Los Van Van	Andy Narell	Paquito D'Rivera	Milton Nascimento
NG La Banda	Mario Bauza	Clare Fischer	Leila Pinheiro
Irakere	Dizzy Gilllespie	Chick Corea	Gal Costa
Celia Cruz	Mongo Santamaria	Sergio Mendes	**And Many More!**

The Latin Real Book Sampler CD

12 of the greatest Latin Real Book tunes as played by the original artists: Tito Puente, Ray Barretto, Andy Narell, Puerto Rico Allstars, Bacacoto, etc.

$16 list price. Available in U.S.A. only.

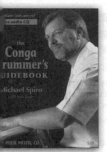

The Conga Drummer's Guidebook By Michael Spiro

Includes CD - $28 list price. The only method book specifically designed for the intermediate to advanced conga drummer. It goes behind the superficial licks and explains how to approach any Afro-Latin rhythm with the right feel, so you can create a groove like the pros!.

"This book is awesome. Michael is completely knowledgable about his subject." – Dave Garibaldi

"A breakthrough book for all students of the conga drum." – Karl Perazzo

Introduction to the Conga Drum - DVD
By Michael Spiro

For beginners, or anyone needing a solid foundation in conga drum technique.

Jorge Alabe – "Mike Spiro is a great conga teacher. People can learn real conga technique from this DVD."

John Santos – "A great musician/teacher who's earned his stripes"

1 hour, 55 minutes running time. $25.

Muy Caliente!

Afro-Cuban Play-Along CD and Book
Rebeca Mauleón - Keyboard
Oscar Stagnaro - Bass
Orestes Vilató - Timbales
Carlos Caro - Bongos
Edgardo Cambon - Congas
Over 70 min. of smokin' Latin grooves!
Stereo separation so you can eliminate the bass or piano. Play-along with a rhythm section featuring some of the top Afro-Cuban musicians in the world! $18.

The True Cuban Bass

By Carlos Del Puerto, (bassist with Irakere) and Silvio Vergara, $22.

For acoustic or electric bass; English and Spanish text; Includes CDs of either historic Cuban recordings or Carlos playing each exercise; Many transcriptions of complete bass parts for tunes in different Cuban styles – the roots of Salsa.

101 Montunos
By Rebeca Mauleón

The only comprehensive study of Latin piano playing ever published.

- Bi-lingual text (English/Spanish)
- 2 CDs of the author demonstrating each montuno
- Covers over 100 years of Afro-Cuban styles, including the danzón, guaracha, mambo, merengue and songo—from Peruchin to Eddie Palmieri. $28.

The Salsa Guide Book
By Rebeca Mauleón

The only complete method book on salsa ever published! 260 pages. $25.

Carlos Santana – "A true treasure of knowledge and information about Afro-Cuban music."
Mark Levine, author of The Jazz Piano Book. – "This is the book on salsa."
Sonny Bravo, pianist with Tito Puente – "This will be the salsa 'bible' for years to come."
Oscar Hernández, pianist with Rubén Blades – "An excellent and much needed resource."

The Brazilian Guitar Book
By Nelson Faria, one of Brazil's best new guitarists.

- Over 140 pages of comping patterns, transcriptions and chord melodies for samba, bossa, baião, etc.
- Complete chord voicings written out for each example.
- Comes with a CD of Nelson playing each example.
- The most complete Brazilian guitar method ever published! $28.

Joe Diorio – "Nelson Faria's book is a welcome addition to the guitar literature. I'm sure those who work with this volume wiill benefit greatly"

Inside The Brazilian Rhythm Section
By Nelson Faria and Cliff Korman

This is the first book/CD package ever published that provides an opportunity for bassists, guitarists, pianists and drummers to interact and play-along with a master Brazilian rhythm section. Perfect for practicing both accompanying and soloing.

$28 list price for book and 2 CDs - including the charts for the CD tracks and sample parts for each instrument, transcribed from the recording.

The Latin Bass Book
A PRACTICAL GUIDE
By Oscar Stagnaro

The only comprehensive book ever published on how to play bass in authentic Afro-Cuban, Brazilian, Caribbean, Latin Jazz & South American styles. $34.

Over 250 pages of transcriptions of Oscar Stagnaro playing each exercise. Learn from the best!

Includes: 3 Play-Along CDs to accompany each exercise, featuring world-class rhythm sections.

Afro-Caribbean Grooves for Drumset

By Jean-Philippe Fanfant, drummer with Andy narell's band, Sakesho.

Covers grooves from 10 Caribbean nations, arranged for drumset.

Endorsed by Peter Erskine, Horacio Hernandez, etc.

CD includes both audio and video files. $25.